BUILDING
TECHNOLOGY
2

CONSTRUCTION TECHNOLOGY AND MANAGEMENT

A series published in association with the Chartered Institute of Building.

This series covers every important aspect of construction. It is of particular relevance to the needs of students taking the CIOB Member Examinations, Parts 1 and 2, but is also suitable for degree courses, other professional examinations, and practitioners in building, architecture, surveying and related fields.

Project Evaluation and Development
Alexander Rougvie

Practical Building Law
Margaret Wilkie with Richard Howells

Building Technology (3 volumes)
Ian Chandler
   Vol. 1 Site Organisation and Maintenance
   Vol. 2 Performance
   Vol. 3 Design, Production and Maintenance

The Economics of the Construction Industry
Geoffrey Briscoe

Construction Management (2 volumes)
Robert Newcombe, David Langford and Richard Fellows
   Vol. 1 Organisation Systems
   Vol. 2 Management Systems

Building Contract Administration and Practice
James Franks

Construction Tendering: Theory and Practice
Andrew Cook

BUILDING
TECHNOLOGY
2

Performance

Ian Chandler

Mitchell · *London*

in association with the Chartered Institute of Building

© Ian Chandler 1989

First published 1989   Reprinted 1992

Typeset by Progress Filmsetting Ltd
and printed in Great Britain by
Dotesios Ltd, Wiltshire

Published by The Mitchell Publishing Company Limited
4 Fitzhardinge Street, London W1H 0AH
A subsidiary of B.T. Batsford Limited

British Library Cataloguing in Publication Data
Chandler, Ian
   Building technology,
   2 : Performance
   1. Buildings, Construction
   I. Title II. Chartered Institute of Building   III. Series
   690

   ISBN 0-7134-5248-X

Contents

Preface

Part One
    Climate and building
      1 Introduction 9
      2 Climate and its Effects on Building 17
      3 Building as a Climatic Barrier 40

Part Two
    Building deterioration
      4 Introduction 75
      5 Materials 84
      6 Construction Form 94
      7 Investigation Procedures 102

Part Three
    Fire technology
      8 Introduction 117
      9 Design of Buildings 122
      10 Fire 132
      11 Passive Fire Protection 139
      12 Active Fire Precautions 148
      13 Means of Escape 152
      14 Fire Safety Engineering 160
      15 Fire Technology 164

Part Four
    Specification
      16 Introduction 177
      17 Standards 186
      18 Bills of Quantity 196
      19 The Role of Specifications 202

Part Five
  Case studies
  20 Five Construction Case Studies   211

References and Further Reading   223
Index   228

Preface

In the writing and production of the three books in the Building Technology series this volume is the last to be published. Volume 3, *Design, Production and Maintenance*, was written first in order to set the topics and issues within parameters which presented clearly the implications of the scope of the subject material. The route was planned and goals determined which provided a final objective. Volume 1, *Site Organisation and Method*, and the present volume complement each other and provide the seeds of topics and issues, together with a more fundamental appraisal of building technology with respect to design, methodology and technological performance. These aspects of the subject are elaborated in volume 3.

The first two volumes present building technology in the context of factors such as safety function, economics, planning, legislation and resources. This analysis continues into *Building Technology 3*; in addition the technology is placed in the wider context of design approaches, change and development in technology and its interface with society and user values. No technology evolves and develops in a social, economic and political vacuum and the topics discussed in this volume must be considered in the context of the millieu within which they grow and interact. It is beyond the scope of this book, and the others in the series, to explain and analyse the reasons underlying the strength of influence of the contextual factors. Only their existence is acknowledged, although a full explanation of their characteristics is given in Part One of *Building Technology 3*. In the development of discussion in the present volume there will be direct and implied reference to these factors as and when appropriate. Ideas and opinions will be presented, both those of acknowledged authorities and those of the author. It is left to you, the reader, to formulate your own ideas and opinions by critically examining the evidence presented. It is quite likely that over a period of time some issues will gain, and others diminish, in importance. It is only possible here to outline the main principles and problems involved, and suggest avenues to follow for solutions. As research proceeds and empirical knowledge grows, new evidence must be used to augment, complement or even contradict that given here. We live in an ever-changing world, in which the process of change is itself speeding up and altering the various social, economic and political factors which must be considered.

There are no absolutely right answers to problems posed in this book: the optimum solution today might be the reject of tomorrow. If there were found to be universally correct answers to the majority of building technology problems, the built environment would become a landscape of uniform structures and components. In the real world, buildings demonstrate a great variety of form, feeling and colour; some are successful, others are not. It is hoped that the principles expounded in this Building Technology series will enable professionals, practitioners and all those concerned with creating the built environment to produce better buildings based on all the available information.

As this is the last book to be written it is appropriate to give grateful acknowledgement and personal thanks to Peter Harlow of the Chartered Institute of Building. He took on the task of editing my manuscripts and converting them into a state ready for publication. He has helpfully criticized style and content and his contribution is invaluable. In addition, Tony Seward of Batsford has put the finishing touches to the books and given needed guidance throughout. Any mistakes and omissions that remain are down to me, while all credit is due to the careful and conscientious work of Sally Matthews and Ann Davies who carried out the typing.

Finally, to all in my family, young and old, I hope it really was not too much of an intrusion upon your hopes, expectations and activities.

Ian E. Chandler

Birmingham
January 1988

Part One
CLIMATE AND BUILDING

1. Introduction

This volume in the series on building technology is the filling in the sandwich of the study. Performance is a fundamental concept underlying all human activity. Judgements on it are made continuously by all members of society, in the form of gossip and news comment or scientific analysis and evaluation. To understand performance, quantifiable or objective criteria need to be used so that standards can be ascertained and comparisons made. The performance of buildings and of those people that contribute to their construction, is of vital importance to the well-being of industrialised nations. It is through the effective use of well-planned, well-built, functional, safe and durable buildings, that a nation's wealth can grow. The building as a whole must perform efficiently to enable human activity to transcend the restrictions of environment. Each element, service and material must in its own right perform adequately and contribute to the whole. It is necessary, therefore, to be able to predict accurately the performance of a building.

A dictionary definition of performance is 'the execution of a command' or 'the carrying into effect of a task'. The task of buildings and their constituent parts is manifold, but the major objective is the provision of protection for the occupants from the vagaries of the climate. In so doing, an internal environment is created which allows allocated activities to take place. The later sections of this volume address the problems involved in determining the performance of a building with respect to climate, deterioration and fire, but initially some ideas underlying the concept of performance are presented. These are followed by a discussion on knowledge with regard to building technology and its meaningful study and application.

In the first and, especially, the third volume of this series, a number of conceptual factors have been introduced and discussed in relation to their effect and influence upon solutions in building technology. As a reminder, these conceptual factors are as follows: *functional requirements*; *safety, economic planning and legislative factors*; *resource availability*; *approach to design*; *technological change and development*; *society/technology interface*; and, finally, *user values*. In the following chapters, these factors will be either explicitly introduced or implied. For example, in Chapter 2 the factors of functional requirement and resource availability, as well as those economic, planning and legislative factors embraced in the approach to design, will be seen to determine the construction of, say, an internal wall to a building. Safety is often a paramount factor in building technology, but user values, economics and technological change play a large part in moulding the approach to fire safety measures. Specifications are affected by the approach to design and are governed by resource availability. Any construction solution is shaped by one or more of the above factors in direct ways, and the reader should be constantly analysing the contents of this volume and placing them within this framework.

One aspect of performance is quality. This is a word which all know, but which is extremely hard to define. The term is frequently used, particularly to evaluate our built environment. For example, a common phrase in the media is 'quality of life'. Is this the same as 'standard of living'? No. A standard of living can be measured, in terms of income, expenditure, property, acquisitions and activities. Quality of life, on the other hand, can be independent of all these factors and measures. Monastic priests might say that they lead lives of the highest quality; they are happy and content. This could also be true of multi-millionaires. A clue to the essence of quality is the concept of 'wants'. 'Wants' are emotions; they arise from within an individual and do not exist as an entity outside that person. Standards can have an independent existence but emotions cannot.

The concept of quality has been explored by Pirsig in *Zen and the Art of Motorcycle Maintenance* (Bodley Head, 1974). The ensuing discussion is based on his ideas and his quest to make sense of two identifiable views of life, both of which influence the perceptions of technology.

Pirsig labels the two views *classic* and *romantic*. The romantic mode is primarily inspirational, imaginative, creative and intuitive. In the classic mode, however, the world is seen in terms of an underlying form, proceeding by reason and by laws. In these terms, motorcycle riding is romantic, while motorcycle maintenance is purely classic. An analogy using piles of sand further explains the division. A classical understanding is concerned with the basics of sorting and relating the piles of sands (as in the addition of sand to a concrete mix). A romantic understanding, on the other hand, is directed towards the pile of sand before the sorting begins.

A figure is on the beach amongst the piles of sand, either sorting them or looking at them. How does this figure relate to the piles of sand? We can answer this by returning to the motorcycle. The 'romantic' rider will see his machine as a series of metal shapes and parts. The 'classic' mechanic, however, looks at the cycle and perceives it in terms of concepts. This idea can also be applied to building technology. A building can be seen in terms of *stability* (foundations), *strength* (structural form), *protection* (internal envelope) and *comfort* (internal services). From these concepts a hierarchy can be formed, with each concept being subdivided into finer parts, and the system forming a coherent whole. While the concern in this series on building technology has been with placing the solution within the contextual framework provided in Volume 3, this is only one way in which to understand technology. A building is an entity consisting of interacting concepts which together form a system that can be judged upon its performance.

To return to Pirsig's ideas, there are two modes of perception – the *classic* and the *romantic*. These might be translated as *objective* and *subjective* respectively. Objectivity involves reason, logic and scientific analysis. Subjectivity, on the other hand, is governed by feelings and appearances. The objective world exists outside a person, who views it subjectively. It can be expressed in terms understandable to all. Pirsig doubts that this is the way to perceive life; there has to be something more than either an objective viewpoint or a subjective viewpoint. His argument finally puts forward 'Quality' as the progenitor of object and subject. The Quality event is the cause of all subjects and objects:

The sun of quality does not revolve around the subjects and objects of our existence. It does not just passively illuminate them. It is not subordinate to them in any way. It has created them. They are subordinate to it.

In other words our very being is based on Quality, but this does not define it. Quality is different from person to person because each of us comes from a different background and has had different experiences, but Quality is made real by the use of analogues, and these analogues are used to define Quality:

We invent earth and heavens, trees, stones and oceans, gods, music, arts, language, philosophy, engineering, civilisation and science. We call these analogues reality. And they are reality. We mesmerise our children in the name of truth into knowing that they are reality. We throw anyone who does not accept these analogues into an insane asylum. But that which causes us to invent the analogues is Quality. Quality is the continuing stimulus which our environment puts upon us to create the world in which we live. All of it. Every last bit of it.

Now to take that which has caused us to create the world and include it within the world we have created is clearly impossible. That is why Quality cannot be defined. If we do define it we are defining something less than Quality itself.

This thought is difficult to comprehend, let alone accept, but it does throw some light on society's relationship to the built environment. Pirsig says that quality is the 'stimulus which our environment puts upon us to create the world in which we live'. In this instance we can direct our attention to just one aspect of the world – the built environment. In this world two approaches can be identified; that of the architect (subjective) and that of the builder (objective). The architect is concerned with shape, size, volume, function and appearance, the builder with materials, labour, plant and money. Generally, the architect develops through an education and training grounded in the arts. The builder rises from a practical trade background and/or through academic study grounded in science and technology. In understanding each of their rules and practices, they develop a language of their own and although each is dealing with the same physical entity – a building – their concepts of it can be very different. It is time that the two approaches drew closer together. One way of effecting such a change is to understand common principles based upon a overriding rationale. This may not be pure 'Quality', as defined by Pirsig, but perhaps a constituent common part of this. Before drawing any conclusions, some further aspects are to be introduced with respect to the integrity of building technology.

Science is said to be exact and definitive, producing clear-cut answers. Unfortunately, this is far from the truth. The purpose of scientific method is the selection of a single truth from among many hypothetical truths. Historically, however, science has done exactly the opposite to this. Through multiplication, diversification and finer analysis, more and more facts, information, theories and hypotheses abound. It is science itself which is leading man from single absolute truths to many-faceted, multiple, indeterminate and relative ones. So, in basing a study of building technology upon a scientific method of enquiry, it is inevitable that a large number of solutions will offer themselves. There will be no one 'right' answer. Some answers, of course, will be more suitable than others, based on criteria within a strict scientific analysis. For example, a softwood can be compared to a hardwood on this basis. But when seen in the context of the other factors, such as economics, function and user values, the choice of wood becomes more complex and indeterminate. The ideal of hardwood is replaced with the reality of softwood. But can 'Quality' be found in both? The answer must be *yes*, but arising from a different practical approach to the same question. The same care and attention can be given to the staging and finishing of softwood as it can to that of hardwood. With proper recognition of properties, each can be adequately protected in exposed conditions. They can perform as well as each other.

Another aspect of life and work is *harmony*. The architect can see harmony in the coming together of concepts such as *strength*, *stability*, *appearance* and *comfort*, expressed in the complete building. The builder can see a quest for harmony in the production of the building, the coming together of the concepts of *productivity*, *efficiency*, *sequence* and *specification*. In so doing, the builder and architect seek facts that most fittingly contribute to this harmony, although it is expressed in terms of two very different sets of concepts. Therefore, it is unlikely that the end product – the building – will be constructed in a manner which ensures a complete resolution. This can manifest itself in poor choice of materials, incompetent design, inefficient sequencing of activities or indifferent workmanship – all leading to defects.

People bring to their assessment a phenomenon: their sense of value. This is discussed fully in Part One, Chapter 9 of *Building Technology 3*, but one aspect pertinent here is the problem of set values. There is a tendency by all of us to set present circumstances, activities, problems and their resolutions in terms of our previous acquired values. It is likely that these have served us well in the resolution of other tasks and they are utilised straight away. In technological terms this is dangerous, especially in this latter part of the twentieth century, when change is continuous and still accelerating. Technological development is not standing still, and neither are society's values. In concrete terms, the building of high-rise blocks of flats was seen as a valuable solution to the housing problem of the 1960s in the United Kingdom. Today, such blocks are being demolished, not only because they have physical defects, but also because society no longer *values* them. As value is changing and relative, but is ever present, it needs to be recognised and accounted for in technological procedures. Science and technology are not value-free. They are created, developed and applied by people who bring to them their own inherent perceptions, hopes and fears.

Pirsig's notion of 'Quality' attributed is beyond definition, yet the construction of buildings is couched in terms of quality. How *can* it be defined? One way is to attempt to describe exactly a translation of quality into recognisable and measurable terms. The format for construction is the production of specifications, either as separate documents or incorporated into bills of quantities. But as will be seen in Part Four Chapter 4, these have limitations. For the moment it is convenient to separate the analysis of building quality into two main concerns: first, the concern for quality in the end product – the building – and secondly the concern for quality in the processes of construction. In both a measure of quality can evaluate performance.

When materials are developed or created, and construction details improved, such work is done on the basis of scientific understanding. In the generation of this understanding, a body of information, data and statistics arises. This is based on common symbols and measures, and can therefore be recorded and retrieved, and used to describe properties and characteristics. In themselves, these properties and characteristics say little about the material or component until it is placed in its location in a building. It is then asked to perform. This performance can be measured and assessed. Does it close the door? The culmination of the work of the designer and the builder (together, of course, with all the other contributors to the building's construction) must be to select and install materials, components and services that perform satisfactorily, and are fit for their purposes. This does not mean that they have to be maintenance-free. In order to retain their levels of performance, maintenance is likely to be essential; it must be seen as a constituent part of performance. By assessing performance levels of an element of a building in use, a measure can be provided to allow assessment and comparison.

Consider now the question of quality in relation to the process of construction. In order to achieve a harmonious working relationship, all the parties involved in the process need to know their aims and objectives,and how they are to be met. During the everyday tasks of design and construction, there needs to be a common denominator of which all will be aware, and which all will use as a basis for determining expectations. Performance can be used as this common link. The designer needs to perform in the production of the contract information; the builder needs to perform in the correct interpretation of this information and to execute it in a satisfactory manner, on time and within cost. Each must have a proper attitude and commitment to the objectives.

The builder can be directly measured in performance: Is the job carried out in a satisfactory manner, completed on time and to the right costs? Has a good service been performed? Many builders obtain work by recommendation or by a previous client returning to them. In these cases, cost is not an overriding issue; satisfactory service is. In other words, the client seeks value for money. Quality and performance go hand in hand.

Clients also demand service from designers. It is not enough to be a good architect or a competent quantity surveyor. Drawings must be produced on time with full information, and specifications and cost analysis should be clear and accurate.

One manifestation of the concern for quality in service as well as in product manufacture and installation is the Quality Assurance Scheme set up by the British Standards Institution. Under this scheme, professional practices and building organisations can introduce procedures which monitor and check the performance of their employees (or systems) in providing an effective and efficient service. These procedures are assessed by Quality Assurance Inspectors; if adequate performance levels are verified then an organisation can claim it meets Quality Assurance criteria. Such a claim alerts the client to the fact that the organisation is aware of the need to question its own activities and personnel, with respect to ensuring that the client gets the best service.

The Quality Assurance Scheme is also applicable to manufacturers of materials or products used in construction. Here, factory procedures are analysed, with checks made on the quality of the products at each stage of their manufacture, not just at the end. The Quality Assurance Scheme ensures the quality of the end product, the building, and the performance of the professionals involved in the process of construction. The philosophy of 'Quality' as conceived by Pirsig might be said to have been translated into a practical system.

This book is concerned with the concept of building performance. Implied in this concept is the notion that quality can be translated into building technology through the integrity of both materials and the people who design and install them. In reading the following pages, think about your attitude to working in construction. Is it just a job that you do? Are you concerned with providing a service to a client and, therefore, to society? Are the economic factors an overriding constraint which dispel any thoughts about providing good quality? Is performance a way in which quality levels can be judged? What part does productivity on site play in achieving specification demands? What responsibility has a building in meeting performance requirements, both with regard to physical properties and to standards of workmanship?

There are no 'right' answers to these questions, as they are influenced by factors which change in emphasis from moment to moment. These questions and many others in the same vein should be borne in mind in the reading of this volume. More importantly, they should be raised in the everyday practice of the construction of the built environment.

The content of this volume, with its emphasis on performance, deals with the substance of construction. *Building Technology 1* was concerned with method in construction. There is a fundamental difference between substance and method. It might be said that substance relates to the form of an atom, while method relates to what the atom does. In construction terms this means that the properties and characteristics of materials and elements do not change. The discussion and description in this book must be seen as complementary to the ideas and principles expounded in *Building Technology 1*. In order to obtain satisfactory performance, site organisation and method must be carried out to the highest levels of integrity and competence, using all available knowledge and experience.

QUESTIONS

1. Discuss the concept of performance with respect to building function.
2. Discuss how the construction industry can respond to changes in value in society.
3. Is it feasible to expect that technological solutions can be based on a full understanding of the influencing factors?

2. Climate and its Effect on Buildings

CLIMATE DESCRIPTION

Buildings are immobile structures set in a changing, complex and damaging environment. This environment may demonstrate a relatively constant nature throughout the year, and from year to year, or conversely, in another place the full range of climatic conditions can be experienced within a year. A knowledge of the prevailing weather of an area is essential for the correct design and construction of any building in that area.

The science of the study of climate is still being developed. Although prediction of general weather patterns over relatively large areas is becoming more accurate, knowledge of many aspects of its full effect on buildings is only slowly advancing. Little understanding has been gained of the effect of wind around buildings, and the manner in which buildings create their own local climatic conditions. The application of computers has greatly enhanced the forecasting ability of the meteorologists and it is now common to see computer-based simulations of the general weather patterns presented on television as part of the weather forecast. It will be noticed, however, that forecasters are always careful to say that local variations may occur. It is important, therefore, to realise that different climatic effects can occur within a general pattern, under the influence of local conditions. The overall weather patterns form a framework which is influenced by local and regional geographic factors; these in turn can produce a climate influenced by the buildings themselves. An example of this is the formation of fog and haze over cities. On an extremely local scale, climate can also be affected by particular details of a building. A roof parapet may create wind patterns which cause damage to coverings. The parapet may be oriented so that deep, shaded areas are created, causing large temperature differences to occur across the building. The result may be excessive differential movement, caused by differing expansion and contraction rates, leading to material failure.

The various levels of climate are identified below.

Macroclimate

Macroclimate is normally described by using data from a number of standardised sites over a large area such as a country or continent (or part thereof). In the UK sets of tables and maps are available giving basic weather information. This is based on data collected over a period of years from a number of weather stations. As an example, a chart can be produced giving the average rainfall, per annum or per month, for all areas of the British Isles.

Mesoclimate

Within a small area, of, say, four kilometres square, climate can vary. For example, a hill will have a south-facing aspect and a north-facing aspect, and such topographical features influence the climate. Hills, according to their steepness and height, can produce variations. In 1985 a housing estate in Sheffield built by the local authority on a hill which was exposed to strong winds was demolished. There were major problems in keeping the weather out as the designers specified inappropriate materials and construction details. It was found to be cheaper to demolish the houses than to improve the cladding – which could not be guaranteed to solve the problems. In this case the designers either failed to find out about the local climate from the regional meteorological office, or chose to ignore this information when designing the houses.

Microclimate

The building and its site can produce climate variations within and about its boundaries, to, say, points drawn 100m from the centre. The chosen orientation of the building can be affected by consideration of these factors. The positioning of the main entrance, or the location of living or working rooms may depend upon this.

Cryptoclimate

As mentioned above, the detailing of a building's elements, components or finishings can lead to the creation of an individual climate, causing, for example, the formation of cold spots, or areas of wind swirl and excessive rain water run off. Unfortunately, the prediction and, therefore, prevention of these occurrences is quite difficult. They are difficult to simulate at the design stage as a precise analysis of the microclimate is required. Currently, there is not enough information available to be used as a basis for such an analysis, let alone to make predictions. The best approach is probably to build a full size model. However, this is costly, and in addition will not necessarily recreate actual conditions. For example, to simulate the climate around a parapet wall it should be modelled on a mock building at the height where it is to be positioned. Possibly the development of computer software will allow detailed analysis of the effects of climate on a building at the design stage. There is much concern with the use of energy in buildings and it is to be hoped that developments in the design of elements to minimise the use of energy will also draw attention to the need to consider, more exclusively, the building and its climate. Figure 1.1 shows the relationship between levels of climatic data and levels of predictability.

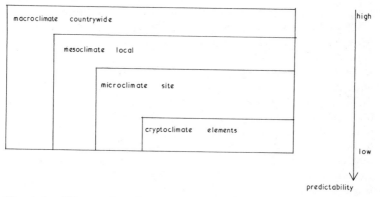

Fig. 1.1   *Climate classifications*

The emphasis in the foregoing descriptions of climate has been on its effects on design and on a building's performance in use. No less important is the effect of weather during the construction process. Knowledge of the weather is important to the builder for two reasons; firstly, because it affects the overall planning and timing of the work, and secondly because it can determine the use and positioning of equipment and plant.

In the first case, weather can directly influence the time of commencement and overall duration of a project. If at all possible, builders like to avoid undertaking ground works during seasons of high rainfall as this can lead to problems of ground instability, difficulties in the movement of vehicles and restriction in work activities. Excessive delays due to inclement weather can seriously affect the profitability of contracts, or increase costs unnecessarily if it is not fully taken into account during the planning stages. Under certain conditions, such as heavy frost, some operations (e.g. placing concrete) cannot be carried out without extensive precautionary measures. Reference to the records indicating local weather patterns will help in planning, enabling an allowance for non-productive days to be built into the projected construction period.

The second case is perhaps not always given the full considera-tion it deserves. For example, the knowledge that tower cranes are affected by wind is common, and care is taken preceding their use in winds gusting at over 48kph, when they cannot be left to slew at will overnight. But what about the position of the crane on site? Generally, a crane is positioned with reference to its ability to cover a certain area and lift particular loads. The optimum placement according to these operational criteria might, however, put it in the spot with dangerously high greatest wind exposure. The effect of this may be a drastic curtailment of the times of operation, or a problem with the control of lifted items.

A building itself can create cryptoclimatic conditions, too, which can affect the construction process, as when cold spots affect the curing of wet finishes.

A general factor pertaining to the climate is the necessity of adequately protecting unused materials and components, and finished, but exposed, work. There are, unfortunately, many examples of poorly protected materials. Although these do not necessarily cause major problems or failures, they do result in a lowering of standards and a raising of the level of maintenance needed. Partly completed buildings with exposed elements can cause particular problems. For example, one can take the case of the multi-storey block of flats in which excessive moisture was found dripping from the ceilings shortly after occupation. Initially, this was thought to be caused by leaking pipes. As the problem persisted, and was experienced throughout the building, it was then thought that the water was permeating through the precast concrete floors from outside, a not uncommon problem. No significant leaks could be found, however. On investigation it was discovered that by drilling into the ceiling up to the floor beams volumes of water were released. The water was lying in the hollow tubes of the precast floor slabs. It had not entered via the external fabric of the building and could only have accumulated during the construction period. Records showed that there had been an unusually high rainfall at that time, and that the construction of external cladding followed the construction of the frame and floors. In the interim, rain had been allowed to seep into the floor units. Once the floors had been drilled and the water released there was no further trouble.

CLIMATIC FACTORS

There are a number of measurable factors which create a climate. Climates will vary from place to place as a result of the different strengths and weaknesses of these constituent factors, which are described in the following sections.

Air temperature

In the UK air temperature is normally recorded at a height of 1.2m above ground level. (Ground level is relative to sea level, and in most places throughout the world it will be above sea level.) The thermometers used for this purpose are shielded from radiation from the sun by day, from neighbouring objects and from the ground; they are also shielded from loss of heat to the cold ground and sky at night. Further, they are protected from precipitation, although the free passage of air is still allowed. Four thermometers are used; two are self-registering to record the maximum and minimum temperatures, one is a 'dry bulb' and one is a 'wet bulb' (see following section for explanation).

Data from the thermometers can be collected daily, or hourly if necessary. Cumulative frequency curves can be plotted monthly to show the percentage variation from the mean temperature for a particular location. The temperature can also be shown by 'contour lines' based on the axis of time of day against month. To show variations from one part of a country to another it is best to use maps superimposed with 'contour lines' representing the average temperatures. A separate map will be necessary for each month to show clearly the range.

Humidity

Humidity is usually measured by a pair of exposed thermometers, placed side by side, one a wet bulb and the other a dry bulb. The wet bulb will generally be recording a lower temperature than the dry bulb owing to the evaporation of the water from the muslim surrounding the end of the bulb. The air's humidity is deduced from the two readings.

Air humidity measurements can be expressed in a number of ways and a building designer must be sure to select the appropriate information to solve a particular design problem. *Vapour pressure* is the partial gaseous pressure exerted by the water vapour, usually expressed in millibars. *Moisture content* is expressed in kilogrammes of water vapour per kilogramme of dry air. This is equivalent to the *mixed ratio*, which is the ratio of the mass of water vapour to the mass of dry air. There are three terms used for expressing the mass of vapour per unit volume of moist air: *vapour concentration*, *vapour density* and *absolute density*. *Relative humidity* is the actual vapour pressure expressed as the percentage of the saturation vapour pressure at the same temperature. The temperature at which saturation is reached, when air is cooled and condensation occurs, is called the *dew point*.

It is most useful to record absolute humidity values, expressed in terms of vapour pressure, dew point or moisture content. Some problems in buildings, however, can be linked with relative humidity levels, as in the case of the equilibrium moisture contents of organic substances such as timber. Relative humidity statistics, without corresponding dry bulb temperatures, give no information about the absolute moisture content of the air.

Atmospheric vapour pressure and relative humidity can be shown as 'contour lines' on maps produced as monthly records.

Precipitation: rainfall, snow, hail

Rainfull is measured by collection in a standard rain gauge on selected sites. There are problems in collecting rain in mountain and moorland terrain as strong winds in these regions can affect the accurate measurement of water in the gauge. Rainfall is expressed as the depth of water (in millimetres) which has fallen into the gauge aperture since the time of the last reading. In the UK rainfall measurements include precipitation from rain, drizzle, snow, sleet and hail. Small amounts of moisture from dew, hoar frost, rime and wet fog also collect in the gauge aperture and contribute to the measurement. Any frozen precipitation is thawed and again included as measured rainfall.

The topography of a terrain can influence precipitation. More hilly or mountainous areas generally have the highest levels of rainfall, for example. Within a relatively small area, large variations in precipitation levels can be found. From year to year, moreover, rainfall levels at any one place can vary quite dramatically (in which case the provision of drainage and water supplies needs to recognise those fluctuations).

Rainfall statistics can be presented in a number of forms:

(a) *rain days*: the number of 24-hour days per annum upon which rain fell, recording a reading of 0.2mm or more; this information can be shown as contours on a map
(b) *average annual rainfall*: this information can be averaged out from a record of rainfall over a number of years; contours superimposed on maps can illustrate this information
(c) *rainfall intensity*: the amount of rain falling within a short

period of time is of importance in the design of drainage: the frequency of this intensity also needs to be considered

Snowfall data in the UK is included in the rainfall statistics, but can be presented in terms of:

(a) the number of days with snow falling on low ground
(b) the number of days with snow lying
(c) the frequencies of difference snow depths

It is also important to know the possible depth of snow, which will not be even owing to the wind causing drifting in the lee of buildings or obstacles or in hollows and cuttings. The density of snow can vary, and it is noteworthy that the duration of snow cover depends greatly on altitude.

Hail falls can be recorded as a number of days per annum and the months during which they occur. Hail stones can cause significant damage, and some severe storms have been recorded in the UK.

Lightning strikes are more common than hail storms but there are no statistics available for the UK. Lightning can cause damage to buildings: it was thought that a strike during a rain storm set fire to the roof of York Minster in 1985, causing millions of pounds' worth of damage.

It is useful to know the rate of evaporation following precipitation. In winter this may be negligible but in summer it can be very high. Wind can increase the rate of evaporation, as can heat leaking from buildings through walls and roofs. Vertical wall surfaces are likely to give greater rates of evaporation as they can absorb much more solar radiation than the horizontal ground (because they take up the rays reflected from the ground in addition to direct solar rays).

Wind

Wind speed is normally measured by an anemometer, usually a system of cups rotating about a vertical axis revolving in direct proportion to the wind speed, although electronic anemometers are also available. The direction of wind can be measured by a vane. Gusts with durations of three seconds or more can also be recorded.

The anemometer is usually placed 10m above the ground, with no appreciable obstacles, including larger trees or hedges, within 200m. Normally, there is a vertical gradient to wind speed, beginning at zero at the lowest surface and rising rapidly in the first few metres until between 300 and 500 metres above the ground it will once again be zero. The general weather situation will determine wind speeds above this height. The rougher the underlying surface the greater the slowing down of the lower layers and the higher the disturbance. Each layer of air creates frictional resistance which results in the slowing of the wind speed. Gusts of wind are also a function of the degree of surface roughness.

Wind speed is presented as an annual average hourly mean recorded in metres per second, which can be plotted as a contour line on a map. Unfortunately, there are difficulties in recording the mean speed of the wind as it is not always possible to position the anemometer in an ideal place. Generally, in towns the wind speed is lower than that found in open country, but in certain situations buildings can sharply increase wind speed.

Monthly statistics are produced to show mean wind speeds, but it is also important to know the amplitude and frequency of gusts, as these are likely to affect a building more than a constant wind. A particular area may have a high level of calms and light winds, but also experience very strong and frequent gusts.

Wind direction is affected considerably by topographical features, and this should be considered fully in the planning of estates and towns. It is also very dependent upon the season of the year.

The frequency of gales is also recorded in the UK. A gale is said to occur when the mean wind speed exceeds 17.2 metres per second for a period of at least 10 minutes. Generally, winds are likely to be stronger on a coast than in the interior of a country.

Sunshine and solar radiation

Sunshine levels can be measured in terms of (a) the total length of burn (or burns) over the day, and (b) the amount of short wave radiation falling on a horizontal surface in a particular period. The total short wave radiation can be measured too, as radiation occurs with a diffuse sky as well as a clear sky.

Statistics can be gathered to show the times of sunrise and sunset. The duration of sunshine hours can be shown on a daily basis, again related to different latitudes. This information can then be presented on maps with contour overlays.

The path of the sun will vary with the time of the year. Diagrams with transparent overlays can be produced to indicate the effects of the sun's angle of incidence and radiation intensity on a building, allowing calculation of the sizes and positions of windows and shading devices. Computer programs are available which are comprehensive in their consideration of all the factors involved in establishing the solar intensities on vertical, sloping or horizontal surfaces for a given latitude. They will take into account, for example, atmospheric clarity, cloudiness and ground reflection.

The intensity and amount of sunshine can vary from morning to afternoon. For example, in the UK there is a tendency for afternoon sunshine to exceed that of the morning.

The measurement of solar radiation is important as it can dramatically affect materials with a low heat capacity. About 99% of the solar energy reaching the earth is in the short wave band, of which 50% is in the visible range. Ultraviolet radiation, for example, is at $0.4\mu m$ wavelength, which is between 0.29 and $4.0\mu m$ (the short wave band). Although this intensity is small it can have an appreciable effect on paints and plastics. It can be excluded, however, by common window glass.

The atmosphere scatters radiation and this forms diffuse radiation from the sky. Sky conditions can be classified into a number of categories, according to the type and amount of cloud present.

It is important to note that the brightest days are not necessarily the hottest days. In the UK collected data has shown that on 'hot' days (when the temperature exceeds 29.5°C) solar radiation levels are not in the order of the highest recordings. There is no correlation between high temperatures and high solar radiation. Temperatures on days of high solar radiation ranged between 16°C and 29°C. It would be erroneous, therefore, to design a cooling system to cope with the simultaneous occurrence of very high temperatures and large amounts of solar radiation.

Although there may not be recorded sunshine on all days of the year there will still be a degree of illuminance. Hourly mean illuminance has been computed for a range of latitudes over the UK. These values for outdoor illuminance can be employed in the design of windows to allow natural daylight to enter buildings.

Atmospheric pollution

Recent research has highlighted the effect that atmospheric pollution has on the climate. Fog and smog are well known manifestations of pollution. Acid rain, although its exact cause is still controversial, is a result of chemical pollutants being carried into the atmosphere from which they are precipitated with natural rainfall. The general weather type will affect the concentration and drift of pollution.

Local climatological conditions

As previously noted, mesoclimate and microclimate can be at variance with general conditions. The factors creating such a variance can be one or more of the following:

(a) *Hills and valleys* in close proximity to each other will have different climates. For example, the mean temperatures on a hilltop will be a little lower than those in a valley, but there may well be more sunshine on the hilltop. The valley's climate is particularly dependent on whether its topography helps or hinders the flow of air. Hollows in the base of a valley can hold cold air, giving much lower temperatures than the surrounding levels or slopes.

(b) *Different soil types* and their *vegetation* can affect the local climate owing to their different thermal capacities and conductivities. Increased moisture and compaction will increase the two foregoing physical properties.

(c) *The presence of water* at coasts, lakes and rivers can influence the climate. Areas just inland from coasts are prone to winds, and large expanses of water can moderate the temperature and prevent frosts by encouraging breezes due to the temperature differential between land and water.

(d) *Trees and woods* tend to increase relative humidity levels and decrease wind speeds.

(e) *Towns* can produce climatic variations by the production of atmospheric pollutants. At night, temperatures tend to be higher than the surrounding countryside owing to the release of solar heat stored during the day by the buildings. Mean wind speeds can be much lower than in the countryside, but buildings can produce their own wind regimes. General comfort levels may be lower in towns than in the countryside owing to the relatively lower wind speeds and the increase in radiant temperatures of the buildings.

An excellent detailed explanation of climatic factors can be found in *Climate and building in Britain* by R.F. Lacy, published by the Department of the Environment (HMSO, 1977).

CLIMATE AND BUILDINGS

The terms *mesoclimate*, *microclimate* and *cryptoclimate* will now be applied to the design and construction of buildings.

Mesoclimate

In the planning of estates – and even perhaps when considering new towns or major expansion to an existing town – it must be remembered that local weather conditions can influence the following aspects of design:

(a) *Layout of roads and public spaces*. The road layout creates the pattern within which the buildings are set. To a certain extent it will determine the orientation of the buildings. The positioning of the public spaces will be in relation to the buildings, their use (for sport, leisure, etc.) and the general climatic conditions over the seasons of their use. What influence will wind speed and wind direction have on the public space? Will note need to be taken of the path of the sun? What effect might the combination of wind and rainfall have? What effect might the public space have on the local weather?

(b) *Zoning of uses.* The siting together of buildings according to their use is common in town planning; this principle is applied to both existing and new plans. Factories may be sited together, with commercial buildings in another area, dwellings in another and shops in yet a further zone. Where should the factories be placed in order that any emanations from them will not spread over the other areas? Wind speed and wind direction will need to be considered here. Commercial buildings tend to be taller than average. How will the climate be affected by them? Will there be overspill effects on to the surrounding areas?

(c) *Provision of landscaping.* Existing features such as woods can affect any buildings in their vicinity. The introduction of vegetation can, in time, slightly change the local climate. For example, landscaped gardens will increase the moisture content of the air. The planting of trees can be used deliberately to affect the climate. They can provide shade from the sun and alter wind speed and direction.

(d) *Siting in relation to topographical features.* Valleys and hilltops will have their own peculiarities. Valley bottoms can have lower temperatures at night; they hold cloud and can therefore be damp even though the surrounding area is in hot, bright sunshine. Hills, ridges, etc. can channel and direct the wind. Rainfall can vary from one side of a hill to the other. Close proximity to water, whether in the form of a lake, a river or the sea, will produce variations from the general climatic conditions over the larger area.

(e) *Size and scale of buildings.* Small, low buildings will have a minimal effect on some aspects of the climate, such as wind speed and direction, but could have a measurable effect on others, such as temperature. The mean temperatures in towns tend to be higher than those in the surrounding countryside. Large, tall buildings can create local winds which can be faster than those generally found in the area. This may cause further variations in air temperatures.

Generally speaking, mesoclimatic conditions can be usefully

analysed to determine their effect on towns. The two most important factors are *air temperature* and *wind speed and direction*. Other factors such as *level of contaminants* (for example, gaseous admixtures), *cloudiness, relative humidity,* and *levels of precipitation* and *radiation* can also be relevant. When a town's site was originally selected, perhaps in antiquity, the local climate might have been different. The town may have developed because of its suitable climate, and this climate may not be appreciably different if the town's buildings did not exist. Some research has established some possible differences in the climatic factors. For example, as regards temperature, the average winter minimum in a town can be 2°C more than that of the surrounding countryside. The annual mean wind speeds can be as much as 30% less.

A reliance on statistics does not give a true picture of how people experience the effects of the weather, however. Buildings themselves may cause a person to feel uncomfortable in hot conditions. They may become hotter than the people inside them, and if the air movement is less than in the surrounding areas, the body will not be able to undertake adequate cooling measures.

There is a definite connection between the height of buildings and the behaviour of winds, especially if there are other buildings in the vicinity. Even relatively low buildings grouped together can create conditions where wind speed and gusts deter people from frequenting shops, for example. The wind can swirl waste paper, make the use of umbrellas difficult, disrupt clothing and even blow people over. The wind chill factor can be increased locally owing to the air flows around the buildings. (Fig. 1.2 shows a typical pattern for air flow around a building.) Additionally, tall buildings may act as a 'scoop' for high level winds and bring them down to ground level. Designers are now taking greater care over the location of tall buildings in towns, but it is difficult to predict their success in controlling local climates. In the first place, it is necessary to have a full picture of the existing climatic conditions, and at the local level this may not be available. Reliance upon data from a meteorological station some kilometres away can be unsound, as it is possible – for reasons already outlined – that the area in question is measurably different in terms of all or a number of climatic elements. One way of determining the flow of air is to build a scale model of a building in its environment and then set it in a wind tunnel. If this is done the wind speed must be simulated with respect to height, as speeds increase from ground level upwards. The main determinants of local winds are the height and breadth of the tall building or buildings.

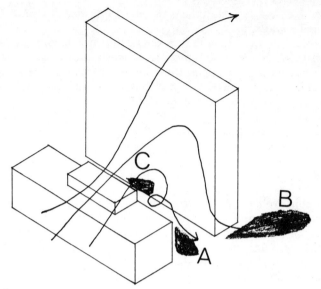

A   subject to strong winds when wind blowing from low to high
building

B   subject to strong winds with almost all wind directions

C   wind blowing to two main faces of the building

Fig. 1.2   *Airflow around tall buildings*

Microclimate

The detailed design of buildings, their orientation, room uses and
layouts, their materials and the construction and positioning of the
main elements, must be governed by a knowledge of climate.
There are two main criteria that will need to be satisfied. First, the
building's users must be protected from the effects of the climate,
and second, this must be done in a way which achieves the desired
levels of comfort with the minimum use of energy. This latter
criterion is of increasing importance as energy is not only
expensive but also finite. Alternative sources of energy other than
gas, coal and oil have not yet been accepted as safe, practical or
economical. Nuclear power still causes worry over safety standards; solar energy is not economic in countries with low levels of
sunshine; the use of windmills may not be practical where wind
speeds are low. The link between building design, service
installation and energy consumption is explored in greater depth in

Building Technology 1, and the concepts are further developed in *Building Technology 3*.

The elements of a building most affected by climate are the external walls and the roof. If there is sufficient knowledge of what climatic factors impinge upon these elements, then the designer will be able to determine the most effective materials and methods of construction to form the best interface between the external and internal environments. A closer look will now be taken at the major climatic factors in relation to the individual building.

Rainfall

A common problem encountered by the users of a building is penetration by rain. This can occur by absorption through porous materials or by direct ingress through cracks and gaps. In order to ascertain the effect of rain on the vertical surfaces of a building, wind speed and direction needs to be considered. The higher the wind speed the greater the probability that rain will enter the building.

Raindrops will tend to fall vertically, but if a wind is blowing it will carry the drops along with it at the same speeds, assuming that the rain drops are of one size and that there is a steady wind. Unfortunately this rarely occurs in practice; consequently, the relationship between drop size and velocity of wind needs to be calculated. A formula has been calculated which combines wind speed and rate of rainfall on to the ground, giving the rate of driving rain (in kg/m^2h). Fig. 1.3 shows, in a simplified form, the effects of wind on buildings.

To illustrate the relationship between wind and rainfall intensity an experiment was carried out by the Building Research Establishment comparing two (unidentified) places in the UK. The main points arising from this study were that at location A the rainfall was around 2.5 times more than at location B, with a wind speed about 50% higher; this gave a total driving rain measurement of nearly eleven times that of location B. Taking the 12 worst days for driving rain for each location, A received about fifteen times as much. The rate of rainfall in location A was not that much higher than location B, but its duration was longer.

This relationship between rainfall and wind speed can be calculated on an annual basis by using annual totals of rainfall and annual mean wind speed statistics. A map (published by the Meteorological Office) has been produced for the UK which shows the annual mean driving rain index as a series of contour lines. These are related to three levels of exposure gradings: *severe*, *moderate* and *sheltered*. The frequency of driving rain intensities and the rate of these also need to be considered. A wind

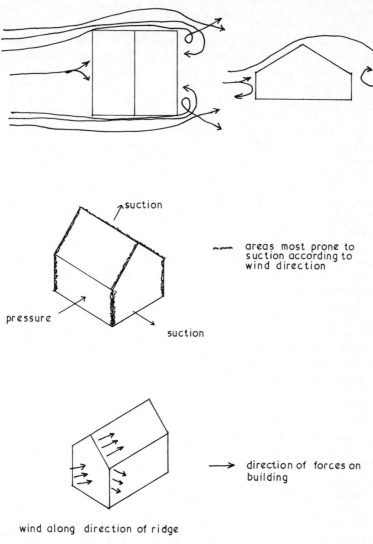

suction

pressure

suction

~~~~~ areas most prone to
suction according to
wind direction

→ direction of forces on
building

wind along direction of ridge

Fig. 1.3 *Winds around buildings*

striking directly on to the face of a building can be used as the basis
of an exposure index, but what might be a severe exposure on a
north face may be classified as severe on a west face in another
part of the country. Local wind conditions and directions,
therefore, need to be considered.

Wind

Wind patterns around buildings have been described when considering the mesoclimate, but for the macroclimate it is the loading effect on the building that warrants attention. The problem lies in the generation of pressures and suctions, illustrated in Fig. 1.3. The distribution of pressure and suction is not uniform, as edges, ridges and eaves are susceptible to particularly high levels of suction. Complete guidance on the use of wind data in design is to be found in the British Standard Codes of Practice. Although maps showing wind speed contours are available for the UK they cannot accurately reflect certain factors at the microclimatic level, particularly the presence of woods, or of areas with buildings up to 10m in height or obstructions up to and above 25m in height.

When a wind hits the face of a building its kinetic energy is converted into dynamic pressure, measured in N/m^2. In addition a combination of wind and rain will exert a pressure on the building's face, and some of this pressure will be directly due to the impact of rain drops.

Suction can remove roofs or coverings along the vulnerable edges of a building. The gusting of the wind causes most problems, and may even set the building oscillating, in a cycle which can be as great as six seconds in the case of a tall building. The taller the building, generally, the greater the period of oscillation. The designer will need to forecast this and integrate it into the calculations for the strength and stability of the building. Stiffening may be required to keep the oscillations at comfortable levels, otherwise the building's users may experience a sense of motion. To avoid discomfort and fear, therefore, no movement should be felt by the building's occupants.

There have been cases where wind has caused whole roofs to be lifted off, or roof coverings to be stripped. As a consequence, roof structures must now be adequately braced (if pitched) and anchored to the structure with metal ties.

The combination of (a) wind, (b) low air temperatures holding unfrozen water droplets, and (c) building surfaces colder than $0°C$ can cause the build-up of rime, perhaps into large sheets. There is an enhanced possibility of icing occurring on tall buildings, especially if located on high ground. In exceptional cases a large build-up of ice can lead to excessive loads being incurred; the design needs to allow for this contingency. In the UK there is a possibility of glazed frosts occurring locally. These are caused by rain falling on to chilled objects such as buildings. Sheets of clear ice are formed, thickest on the windward side, to a maximum of 25mm.

Ice deposits can also originate from fog or cloud, the latter giving a higher rate of deposition. Again, a steady, relatively low wind speed will aid the formation of the ice, but this will be less dense than that formed in fog or cloud.

Solar radiation

The orientation of a building is not only important with regard to the wind direction and, therefore, the possibility of rain penetration, but also with regard to the path of the sun and its seasonable intensity. In the UK the importance of using solar energy as an energy supplement has become increasingly apparent recently. While the necessity of natural lighting has always been considered in the design of buildings, little notice has been taken of the possibility of heat gain from suitable construction on south facing elevations. Glass conservatories, for example, will give extended living areas and also act as heat reservoirs to augment the internal heating. Although large expanses of glass may appear to contribute greatly to heat loss through the walls, they can, if properly designed, produce a positive overall heat gain throughout the year on south facing elevations (in the northern hemisphere). Some shading devices may be necessary during times of intense solar radiation to reduce the probability of overheating.

Degree-days are usually employed as a measure of ascertaining the heating requirements of a building. The calculation of degree-days is based on the assumption that heat loss from a building is proportional to the difference between a base temperature and the mean air temperature during the relevant period. Degree-days are calculated by multiplying the time (measured in days) by the mean temperature difference. The base temperature is assumed to be 2–3°C below the mean air temperature in the building. The reason for this difference is that there will be strong heat gains from, for example, machines, people and solar radiation, which will not incur heating costs. These should not be used in the calculations, therefore. To take an example: an outside temperature of 3°C and an internal base air temperature of 17° (actual temperature 20°C) will give a mean temperature difference of $17° - 3° = 14°C$. For a time period of one day the result will be $14 \times 1 = 14$ degree-days. To obtain the total for a month the mean temperature for that month is used. Therefore, for January with a mean of 4°C (found in the London area) and a base temperature of 17°, 13×31 days gives a total of 403 degree-days. This figure is taken to be proportional to the average heat losses from a building. Therefore, the higher the total, the higher the heat losses, and vice versa. This method is useful for estimating the future energy consumption of a building, but should not be used for the comparison of alternative heating system designs, as it requires a measure of interpretive skill. (For an appropriate method of calculation see the CIBS Building Energy Code, *Part 2: Calculation of energy demands and targets for the design of new buildings and services*, Chartered Institution of Building Services Engineers, 1981.)

Cryptoclimate

Parts of a building, such as parapets, internal corners, overhanging sections and projections can create their own weather patterns. The prediction of these phenomena is difficult to achieve with any measure of success, although some examples will illustrate their effect.

Crystals can form on external walls where temperature differences coupled with flows of polluted water down the face can create their growth. Ice can form on external walls in small areas where there is a combination of water and localised low temperatures. Snow can be blown up under overhanging eaves and remain unthawed long after the surrounding snow has melted. The effect of wind on a building can be accentuated by its profile; vortices can be created, or areas of swirling gusts, which may cause structural damage. The chilling effect of the wind, again in a small area, can be greater than that normally allowed for in the designed exposure levels. This can induce greater heat losses than envisaged through the building's fabric. Solar radiation, even in climates with temperate conditions, can cause local problems. Where extra deep window mullions are used, for example, a shadow may be cast over the window pane, creating a sharp difference in temperature along a line over the glass on days with high solar radiation. This causes differential rates of expansion which may crack the glass. Direct exposure to strong sunlight can also cause plastics to deteriorate, although manufacturers' research is taking this into account in the development of building products for use on external envelopes.

A continually damp wall experiencing relatively low temperatures can create ideal conditions for the growth of lichen, or even mould. Mould growth is encouraged by poor insulation of the wall, creating cold areas.

An extreme range of temperatures from hot to cold can cause a building's fabric to expand and contract over large or small areas. The frequency of change of temperature needs to be considered; the greater the frequency, the more rapid the motion of expansion and contraction, which can lead to material or component failure.

THE CONSTRUCTION PROCESS AND CLIMATE

The foregoing remarks have been made in relation to the design of buildings, but an essential part of the creation of the built environment is the construction process. In this connection there are two main aspects arising from the climate that the builder needs to consider. The first is the effect of climate on materials, components and the partially completed structure of a building. The second is the effect of climate on the methods of construction, the sequence of work and the overall time taken. Here, only a brief introduction will be given to the weather's effect on materials, components and part-build structure, as this will be dealt with in depth in Chapter 2.

On delivery to site, materials need to be checked with their specifications, off-loaded and (usually) stored for some time prior to use or fixing in place. During the storage period materials can be affected by the climate. Therefore, an understanding of the materials' properties and characteristics is necessary for their adequate protection. Reference to local meteorological data will give information on possible rainfall, temperatures, solar radiation, wind speeds, humidity etc. during the time of storage. It is obvious that certain materials are particularly prone to the effects of the weather. Timber must be kept from rain; concrete from frost; and bricks and mortar from excess heat. Plasterboard and cement can be affected by high humidity. Rain and water vapour can cause corrosion on unprotected iron-based components.

Perhaps the greatest problem is to do with the effects of climate on partially completed buildings. Wind can blow down structural walls and framed structures before they are properly tied together if there is a lack of temporary support. This may be due either to a lack of knowledge of what the wind might do, or to negligence in the provision of specified temporary support. Even a little excess movement in unstable structures may cause serious problems, for example in the misfitting of components or the weakening of joints. As the building is being constructed it can in itself alter the local climate, especially with respect to the wind. The builder will need to monitor any changes and prevent them affecting building activities.

The wet trades – plastering, concreting and painting – are especially vulnerable to the climate. Without proper protection, low temperatures can prevent plaster from curing, and high temperatures may dry out the material too quickly. Wind can exacerbate both problems. External paintwork is particularly prone to disturbance by climate. Rain and low temperatures lift the paint film; solar radiation dries it out too rapidly. The backgrounds to these finishes may also be affected by the weather prior to the application of the coverings. The builder must ask: Is the brick wall too dry? How much moisture is there in the timber?

The insertion of jointing material should be made with full regard to the weather. Have the components/units/materials expanded, forming a less than normal width gap? What effect does the weather have on the jointing material? The rule for these and other applied materials is to check the manufacturer's or supplier's instructions regarding the optimum conditions for application. Where none exist, reference should be made to the British Standards organisation, to trade associations or to research institutions such as the Building Research Establishment. Further consideration of materials and climate will be undertaken later. The second aspect of the effects of climate on activities on site will now be explored.

To introduce this topic the following example describes one effect of weather upon construction activity. A private development of a housing estate was made the subject of a feasibility study. The ground was found to consist of a nearly one-metre depth of peat overlaying a sound, load-bearing stratum. The most effective way of dealing with this was to completely strip off the layer of peat to reach the ground below. The total volume of material was calculated and, ultimately, the estimated cost of its removal was ascertained. It was stated in this estimate that the ideal time of year for the removal of the peat was the summer, when rainfall was at its lowest level. Two factors contributed to this decision:

(a) the bulk of the peat would increase if it were saturated with water, thereby increasing transportation costs. (In effect, the lorries would be taking water off-site.)
(b) the excavating machines and transportation lorries would lose efficiency if they worked over waterlogged ground.

In the final analysis the financial feasibility of the development hinged on the budget available for the removal of the peat. To achieve the desired profit margins the work needed to be carried out during the period of least rainfall. The postscript to this case is the unfortunate fact that the work commenced in late autumn, when the peat was saturated and there was little chance of it drying out. Indeed, more rainfall created further excavation problems. This activity went over budget, and the development failed to make a profit.

The moral of this example is that weather can not only affect materials but also totally disrupt construction methods and the sequence in which they are carried out. Much of this disruption can and should be foreseen. It should be taken into account when planning the work methods and in determining the overall sequence of activities.

Useful climatic statistics include data on the following:

(a) *rainfall*: amounts (during daylight working hours), intensity and frequency.
(b) *wind*: reference must be made to local conditions. This information is especially desirable if using a tower crane or building high and lifting components.
(c) *snowfall*: how many days does snow lie on the ground? Snow can hinder access to a site and make work areas unsafe.
(d) *temperatures*: extreme heat or cold can prevent certain activities being carried out, such as concreting or painting. Knowledge of likely forthcoming temperatures will enable proper protective measures to be undertaken. Heavy frost can freeze the ground and prevent its easy excavation. Exposed temporary water-pipes can freeze and unnecessary time and trouble can be spent in thawing them out prior to the day's work.

Generally, the weather can influence the way in which site operatives carry out their work. Wind, rain and low temperatures can slow down their activities, as can a hot and/or humid atmosphere. Levels of productivity can be seriously affected by the climate, even though there is no actual cessation of work. Uncomfortable spots can also be found on site. A building creates its own cryptoclimate which can affect the construction process in that area, even though general conditions do not unduly influence the work. Medical research is being carried out to ascertain the effect of weather upon the health (and therefore efficiency) of building workers. Initial findings show that most workers are inadequately clothed. Other factors may be involved, such as the nature of the physical activity, which is independent of the climate. For example, back problems may be due to bending and lifting loads. This physical activity can be done inside or outside, and cause problems to workers whether they are within a building or out in the open air. Perhaps it is time that all outside workers were required to wear adequate outdoor clothing as a protection against wind chill, the sun or rain. Apart from the obvious health benefits arising from this, there is also the benefit to the employer in ensuring that work efficiency is not impaired by the effects of the climate. There is also an ethical argument for the welfare of the person to be of high priority. Failure to consider the effects of weather on materials and people can drastically affect the levels of quality achieved. Poor protection of materials can lead to rejection by the client's representative, involving the builder in the extra time and costs required to rectify the offending work.

SUMMARY

In *Building: The Process and the Product* (Construction Press, 1978) Harper has widened the elements of exposure beyond merely climatic effects to create four main groups:

Group A: earthquakes; volcanoes; tornadoes; tidal waves; cloud-bursts; floods; avalanches; hailstones.

Group B: sandstorms; blizzards; snow and ice; thunderstorms; atmospheric winds; heat from the sun; drought.

Group C: dimensional movement; condensation; glare; persistent rain; noise; climatic temperature contrasts.

Group D: fire; explosion; local structural failure; surrounding densities; pollution; vandalism.

The incidence of these phenomena is cited against the following three factors:

(a) *frequency*: not in world belt; no known incidence; historic incidence; uncertain – a chance; likely; certain.

(b) *effect on people*: fatal; some survivors; casualties/illness; fear and anxiety; discomfort; no effect.

(c) *effect on buildings*: total collapse; partial collapse; secondary failures; small-scale failures: small-scale fractures; continual maintenance.

The building in question is related to the above phenomena and factors when these are formed into a table, with the elements of exposure forming a list on the vertical axis and the factors listed along the horizontal axis. A simple visual display shows the incidence of the element of exposure and its possible effect. This table can form a starting point in the determination of the climatic effects on a building.

From this detailed information an analysis can be made using information given in this chapter under the headings of *macroclimate*, *mesoclimate*, *microclimate* and *cryptoclimate*. The particular effects of the climate have been presented, including those resulting from temperature, humidity, precipitation, wind, sunshine and solar radiation, atmospheric pollution. The relationship between climate and buildings has been explored and various design factors discussed. Finally, a discussion on the effect that the climate has on the construction process has been presented.

Before any building can be designed and built its location in relation to the climate should be fully ascertained. Information and data should be collected so that in specifying the optimum building envelope the correct materials and construction can be used to form an efficient climatic barrier. This is the topic of the next chapter.

QUESTIONS

1. List the sources available in your geographic location that will provide information on the climate and its effects.
2. To what extent might knowledge of detailed climatic data influence the design process for a building?
3. Discuss how weather information can aid the programming of construction activities.

3. Building as a Climatic Barrier

The previous chapter considered climate and its effect on buildings. In this chapter the role of a building as a climatic barrier, and consequently an enclosure for another climate, will be discussed. The focus will be on the composition of the external fabric and its necessary function and properties. Design criteria, the production of the internal environment, and the interface between the external and internal environments will be discussed. An introduction will be given to some of the modelling tools used for ascertaining the performance of the building in providing the appropriate levels of comfort in relation to the indigenous climate.

GENERAL ASPECTS

The main requirement of a building is that it provide shelter for people. The characteristics and function of that shelter have to satisfy two major criteria: first, that of giving protection against the prevailing climate, and, second, that of providing the appropriate internal environment to suit the activities of the people within it. This latter aspect is discussed in Part Three of *Building Technology 1*, but some further points will be made later when considering the effect of the external wall on the internal environment of a building.

In providing protection against the effects of climate, the external fabric (walls and roof) should be considered with respect to the factors shown in Fig. 1.4. Before considering each of these factors in some detail a few general points will be made.

There is an ever-increasing trend for standards of comfort to be enhanced, whether within buildings or, for example, in means of transport. Man is forever striving to control his environment, particularly in the creation of buildings. So, while the main functional requirements can be identified, their interpretation will vary greatly from building to building under differing ranges of climatic conditions. Components will vary and choices will be made between, for example, the use of fabricated fabric elements and the modification of basic materials into *in situ* panels. High temperatures and long hours of sunlight may mean that the fabric of a building can utilise the climate to reduce internal energy consumption, or even provide basic energy to sustain the

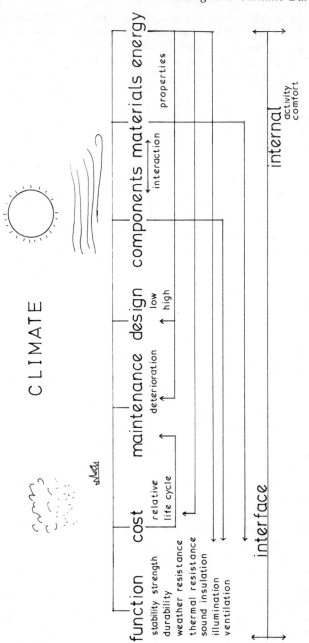

Fig. 1.4   *Climatic barrier factors*

building's services. A building in its own plot can be self-sufficient. (For a full account of how this can be achieved see Vale, B. and R., *The Autonomous House*, Thames and Hudson, 1975.) By recycling the waste products of human habitation a source of methane gas can be generated which can provide fuel for cooking, etc. By carefully orientating the building, the climate can be utilised too. For example, a south-facing wall (in the northern hemisphere) tends to receive larger amounts of sunlight, therefore any solar collecting systems should be incorporated into that façade. Conversely, the northern aspect will face the harsher weather, so such items as glazed windows should be kept to minimal sizes to minimise heat loss and reduce maintenance. Likewise, surfaces on a south-facing aspect need to be able to withstand the effects of the sun, which may cause wide ranges of expansion and contraction in certain materials. Ultraviolet and other rays may also affect wall materials. The design of the fabric, therefore, needs to take into account its desired functions.

As discussed in *Building Technology 1* a number of approaches can be taken to the design of the fabric. A high technology approach, for example, sees the fabric solely as a barrier between the internal environment (created by a sophisticated system of services, such as heating, lighting and air conditioning) and the external, 'hostile' climate. Certain useful properties of the 'hostile' climate may be tapped at the interface between the internal and external environments. Such features as passive solar glazing structures will be integrated into those walls in most contact with the sun.

It is of little worth if an external wall requires constant maintenance, so this must be kept to a minimum. Materials, components and methods of construction must be designed and integrated to require the least maintenance, therefore. (The deterioration of buildings is discussed in greater detail in Part Two, pp.75–116.) A major consequence of undertaking maintenance is the cost incurred, and it is a major reason for endeavouring to minimise it. A wider discussion of the interrelationship of design, production and maintenance is presented in *Building Technology 3*.

A direct comparison can be made between two components, or between a component and an *in situ* production using raw materials. For example, a precast, factory-made, concrete panel may be compared with one cast from steel reinforcement, cement, aggregate and water in a mould placed *in situ*. Different on-site production processes have different costs and these must be considered in the overall cost analysis.

The foregoing issues will be addressed again in this chapter after a detailed investigation of the factors listed under the heading of *function* in Fig. 1.4.

FUNCTION

The prime consideration in the provision of a barrier against the climate must be the shielding of the building's occupants from the effects of the weather. Function should override all the other factors shown in Fig. 1.4. If the weather cannot be prevented from interfering with the internal activities, then the external fabric is useless. Despite many years of experience and scientific research the design and construction of a building's external envelope often fails to meet its basic functional requirements. Even buildings which have gained major architectural awards have shown signs of fabric failure soon after occupation.

There is sufficient knowledge available on the basic properties of materials, but one major problem is that of effectively testing materials *in situ*, when formed into fabric elements or components. In manufacturing consumer goods, such as washing machines, all the parts, singly and as a whole machine, can be tested to virtual destruction over a relatively short period of time by continuous working. The only effective way of testing building materials is to make them up into the finished structure and then observe them in use. This means that whole buildings, façades or roofs are built and then monitored over a number of years. Perhaps within two to three years some indication of performance might be found but buildings are expected to last for up to sixty years or more, so a three-year period might not be long enough to make a valid judgement. If the test is carried out over say ten years, the results would be more valid, but can the costs involved be justified? The initial cost of building test façades (or whole structures) is high. The cost of monitoring will not be cheap, and finally the cost of waiting for ten years before the material, product or component can be used may be large.

Who pays? Is it the material developer, the builder, the architect or a state sponsored establishment? At present the most common sponsor is one of the producers. In the UK the state does sponsor some research into building materials and techniques, but since the late 1970s the level of research has fallen dramatically. Some major building companies have research and development divisions, but their overall contribution is not very significant. The drawbacks for buildings in introducing and testing new materials (or combinations of components) are manifest. Before any commercial organisation invests in research and development it must have some expectation that the new idea will sell, and that the market is large enough to provide sales which will cover initial investment and ultimately generate profit. Material and product suppliers tend to lead the way in research and development as they can sell their products to builders, both nationally and internationally. But they are faced with the same problem of time. For how long can the material or component realistically be tested? Might a rival company produce a similar product first and gain a commercial advantage? On the other hand, if a product is released too quickly and faults occur, the commercial repercussions will be serious. This dilemma is not always satisfactorily resolved and there have been cases of product failures due to insufficient-long term testing.

It would seem possible to simulate the exposure and use of materials or components using a computer, although the number and range of variables needing to be taken into account would be extremely high. One would have to allow for the cumulative effects of, say, frost and sun, expansion and contraction, internal pressure, and of surface tension on a brick. In a relatively porous brick the effects of this over many years can be seen in the form of surface spalling, but it is unlikely that a simulation could effectively reproduce this, or establish the number of winter/summer cycles before the brick crumbles away to dust. Again, who will finance this simulation? The brick maker, the supplier, the user or the state? Indirect state funding, together with commercial sponsorship, could be directed towards universities and polytechnics. In this way research students, teaching staff, product companies and, finally, the customer and user would all benefit.

In the foregoing discussion a relatively simple physical property, that is porosity, was used to illustrate a possible test simulation using computers. It is at this level of basic understanding that building as a climatic barrier should be seen. Some of these basic properties are listed below. The reader is expected to know what these mean with respect to the common building materials and to have some scientific understanding of them.

(a) *Porosity*. If the material can take in fluids, how far can they enter? Can they be expelled easily? What happens if they are retained? What effect will this have on the expansion and contraction of the material, and, therefore, on adjoining materials? How will a completely non-porous material react with the weather?

(b) *Capillarity*. Usually coupled with porosity, this will influence the rate of absorption of fluids. In the case of two materials or components abutting each other fluids can progress between them and possibly penetrate into a building. This must be foreseen at the design stage.

(c) *Vapour diffusion*. Most materials will allow some matter to pass through them. The major problem in building is the prevention of moisture entering as vapour, from either inside or outside. Problems of interstitial condensation can arise within the fabric unless this is prevented.

(d) *Moisture and thermal movement*. One of the biggest problems in designing the interface between internal and external environments is in accommodating particular and cumulative movement. This can be caused by moisture in porous materials (or in those affected by oxygenation) or by thermal changes. Does it matter that an external surface will expand and contract at a different rate than an internal surface? What effect will this expansion and contraction have on joints between components? Is it necessary to provide special joints to accommodate movement over large expanses of like material? How is the joint protected against the weather?

(e) *Dimensional stability*. This is a corrollary of expansion and contraction. How necessary is it to maintain dimensional stability? What degrees of movement can be allowed?

(f) *Thermal conductivity*. This property has gained in importance over the last two decades as the need to reduce energy consumption in buildings has increased. How much heat energy does a material allow through it? What is the overall effect of the materials, their relative positions and construction details on the thermal conductivity of the fabric? Will this be affected by building orientation and geographical position? Can the thermal properties of the fabric be utilised in bringing energy into the building?

In Part Two these properties will be considered with respect to deterioration of the building (see pp.75–116).

STABILITY/STRENGTH

First and foremost, any building element must be able to resist any forces imposed upon it. In the case of the external envelope it may have to carry out two functions: first, to carry the load of the building itself, and, second, to resist the load due to the climate, particularly wind. In the first instance the fabric needs to be relatively strong, over and above the necessity of stability under strong wind conditions. Whether or not it is to be load-bearing will influence the choice of materials (with their intrinsic properties) and the methods of construction. It is possible to use one material – for example, concrete – in both a climate-resisting capacity and also a load-bearing capacity. In each case, the strength of the concrete itself, its thickness, degree of reinforcement and method of construction will differ to suit the circumstances. The surface treatment (with its consequent performance) might well be the same. If the envelope is structural load-bearing it must be able to cope with any movement due to the loads, in addition to those induced by the internal and external environments. The structural engineer and building technologist need to work together to ensure that the structural needs can be fitted with the behaviour of the fabric and that each takes cognisance of the other.

WEATHER RESISTANCE

Many demands are placed on the fabric in coping with the physical and chemical effects of climate. The previous chapter described those climatic conditions which affect the building envelope: rain, wind, sun, snow, frost, sleet, with their corresponding variations in air temperature and humidity. The façade will need to resist wind-driven rain which, because of a micro- and/or cryptoclimate may literally travel upwards via joints, gaps or cracks into the building. A decision needs to be made as to what basic method is to be used to deal with rain falling on to the building. Should the materials be allowed to take in and expel water? Or should the envelope act as a shield and shed all the water at its external surface? Should water be allowed to penetrate joints? If so, how can it be drained? What effect might rain, in conjunction with atmospheric pollutants, have on the materials? Will it cause staining or progressive damage? Will it matter if ice forms on the surfaces or within joints? What effect will the sun's rays have on surface coatings? Will colour be affected? The combination of high air temperatures and high humidity can cause problems of entrapped moisture within the façade's structure if vapour penetrates. Are there sufficient safeguards to prevent this occurring?

Some relatively simple tests can be carried out to ascertain the behaviour of materials and construction details under simulated weather conditions. One test, conducted by the Building Research Establishment, showed that water directed horizontally and at force (as though wind-blown) against a single-skin, standard-facing brick wall would after a relatively short period of time penetrate the wall and run down the internal face. The bricks become saturated and, therefore, the force of the water on the surface expels the surplus onto the other side.

Tests carried out on joints between pre-cast concrete panels have demonstrated the merits of open joints. (See BRE current papers 89/94, *Open-jointed rain screen*; 86/74, *Window to wall joints*; 81/74, *Some observations on the behaviour of weather protective features on external walls*; and 65/74, *Tolerances and fits for standard building components*.) Although evidence on the small scale can be gathered regarding particular aspects of weather resistance there is virtually no long-term research being carried out on whole building structures. Progress regarding improving weather resistance has been largely empirical, relying on mistakes to provide the evidence. It is only when failures occur that remedial action is taken – and lessons learnt. Unfortunately, these failures take place in buildings in use and can have a disruptive effect on their occupants.

In the UK a massive problem has emerged with regard to the structural stability and weather resistance of many system-built houses and multi-storey flats. The amount of remedial work involved in curing weather penetration problems is immense. In Birmingham (England) alone there are 70,000 dwellings which are suffering, to a greater or lesser degree, from the effects of poor design, materials and workmanship on their ability to provide adequate shelter from the climate. A Manpower Services Commission (Training Commission) sponsored project (the Birmingham Project: Training for Evaluation and Repair of Non-Traditional Buildings) will identify the major faults and produce learning materials for organisations, both national and international, faced with maintaining buildings with such problems. This will give some clear guidance on the technological options open to ensure valid weather resistance.

Some multi-storey blocks of flats have been completely reclad. The basic structure and cladding is untouched, new windows are installed in a sheet-metal skin with a protective coating. The skin is reinforced with vertical, lightweight, metal beams acting as external 'stiffeners'. The whole cladding is attached to the building using non-ferrous fixings. It will be interesting to see how this solution works over the years. The architectural style is clean and high-tech, giving the building a streamlined appearance, and can be seen as an improvement over the original drab concrete. It is to be hoped that the performance, as regards weather resistance, matches the visual upgrading.

An important factor contributing to failure in weather resistance is identified in Fig. 1.5, i.e. workmanship. This factor will be reconsidered in the discussion of deterioration on pp.75–116. The factors on the left of the diagram have already been discussed in Chapter 2. Using research evidence published by the BRE (current paper 86/74, *Window to wall joints*, M.R.M. Herbert) an example shows how construction details can affect the weather

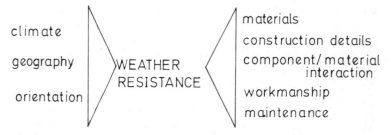

Fig. 1.5 *Factors affecting weather resistance*

resistance, in this case of a joint. If the seal is placed flush with the surface of the adjoining components no protection is afforded. Therefore the joint is completely exposed to elements of the weather such as solar rays, wind-blown rain, etc. It can suffer from quite rapid changes in temperature and be physically damaged by sleet. If the seal is recessed 50mm from the faces of the components, however, the majority of the water will drain away before reaching the seal, thereby protecting it. If protrusions are made on the surface of the components adjacent to the joint this will prevent water from the component's face being driven on to the seal. There may be also an advantage arising from the possibility that these protrusions will give shade to the seal from direct sunlight. If such protrusions are used they must be in a durable material which in itself is not adversely affected by the weather.

There are many types of seal available to suit particular circumstances, but the ideal seal configuration and design has not yet evolved. To quote from the BRE current paper:

In discussion, many window and sealing compound manufacturers agree that some details in common are unsatisfactory and they would like to see them changed. However, they are in a highly competitive market so the need to tender competitively for jobs can over-ride their wish to see the best technical solution adopted. For this reason they considered that little technical improvement, if it involved extra cost, was likely to stem from the industry. A number of manufacturers mentioned that the require-ments for architectural effect, e.g. flush exteriors to façade, often conflicted with good technical detailing, especially when their standard products were used. It is said to be manufacturers' experience that clients or professional advisers were not generally prepared to incur the extra cost of modifications to provide technically good solutions for these situations.

This state of affairs does not augur well well for ensuring that a successful interaction between components and materials is achieved. Problems can arise with: dimensional change incom-patability; chemical incompatability (causing degradation of the component or material); or the failure to achieve an effective physical joint between the component and material. Two exam-ples illustrate these problems. Thin brick slips were glued on to a concrete lintel to ensure that the façade was seen totally as brickwork. After a short time the brick slips fell off. Initially it was thought that the adhesion was sufficient, but although this was found to be the case, it was not causing the failure. The cause was found to lie in the different rates of expansion and contraction of the bricks and the slips and the concrete backing. Movement was the result of changes in air temperature due to climatic conditions. The bricks expanded more, and at greater rates, than the slips (which were 'cooled' by the concrete backing) and pushed on to the slips, which were then squeezed, bowing away from the concrete backing, breaking the adhesive bond and, finally, falling off.

A second example is illustrative of chemical reactions resulting in a leaking roof. A flat roof was covered in standard zinc sheet, laid in strips with rolls and drips. Water penetrated this roof and entered the rooms below. This was the first indication of trouble. An inspection of the roof showed that the zinc was pitted with small holes in a line closely corresponding to an overhead telephone cable. This cable was made from copper, and, when inspected during the winter months, was found to be some distance above the surface of the roof. It was thought that electrolytic reaction was occurring, corroding the zinc – but *how*? Rainwater could drip from the cable, but this would not form a circuit, nor would it be strong enough in copper to eat into the zinc. Repairs were carried out and the roof monitored. The problem was solved later when it was observed that as the air temperature increased over spring and summer, so the cable expanded. As it expanded it sagged and actually touched the roof. After a summer rainfall the ideal conditions were created for an electrolytic reaction to occur. To overcome this the cable had to be either re-routed or propped clear of the roof covering.

A relatively durable material such as concrete can withstand most extremes of climate. It can resist atmospheric pollution and physical battering, as exemplified by the remains of Mulberry Harbour on the Normandy coast of France, which was used immediately after the landings in 1944 (see P. Burton, final year B.Sc. Building dissertation on 'Concrete deterioration', Polytechnic of the South Bank 1983). If not produced correctly, however, concrete will not provide weather resistance. A common problem lies in the positioning of the reinforcement. If too close to the external surface, water vapour can penetrate to the steel and activate the process of corrosion. The steel will rust, expand and push off the covering concrete, exposing the bars. Further corrosion can then take place, reducing weather resistance and strength – and presenting an unsightly appearance.

The common softwood used in window- and door-frames in the majority of houses in the UK needs to be fully protected to give it sufficient weather resistance. It therefore requires proper preparation and painting. Paintwork needs to be renewed at least every five years, and on south-facing elevations (in the northern hemisphere) every three years. In exposed coastal areas it may be necessary to repaint every year.

A material in itself, it can be seen, may not be capable of giving the desired weather resistance performance. In concrete, a necessary inclusion (reinforcement) could reduce effectiveness if not placed correctly, and, while softwood as a raw material needs applied materials in order for it to perform satisfactorily. When considering materials for external use, the manner in which they are utilised, the construction processes involved and the possible maintenance needed should be accounted for in the design.

Finally, in assessing a material, component or construction detail for resistance to the weather, consideration must be given to place of use. A material produced and tested in the south of England cannot be employed in the north of Scotland and be expected to perform according to the test results. The local climate must be considered in relation to prevailing circumstances. Under the Building Regulations (1985) it is possible for a national house builder to obtain 'type approval'. In this case, a particular house, with all its attendant construction details and materials, can be built anywhere in England and Wales. This may satisfy the regulations, but will it perform satisfactorily under all local weather conditions? The regulations are only minimum require-ments and it is still incumbent upon the house builder to ensure the weather resistance of the type in its geographical location. This may mean altering some details: for example, recessing the windows rather than building them flush with the external brickwork, thus affording greater protection against wind-driven rain, snow and sleet. The importance of studying local weather conditions should not be underestimated in the design and construction of all buildings.

THERMAL RESISTANCE

In the UK there has been a considerable increase in the thermal resistance required of external envelopes. This was brought about by the massive increase in energy prices dating from the early 1970s. All new buildings (and those being completely refurbished or renovated) now have to meet stringent demands for reducing the transmission of energy from inside to outside. The value of this level of resistance is measured in watts per square metre of envelope for a degree Celsius difference in temperature between internal and external environment, called the 'u' value. This is applied to the overall thickness of the envelope's fabric and is averaged between glazed areas (required for natural lighting and/or ventilation) and the rest of the wall. Separate values are given in the Building Regulations (1985) for walls, floors and roofs. It is quite likely that these statutory values will alter from time to time.

In order to satisfy the 'u' values new materials have been developed to augment the traditional brick, concrete and timber. The required values could be met by increasing the thickness of walls built in traditional materials, but this has three main disadvantages. First, the overall fabric width is increased, which might reduce the internal floor space available. Second, the mass of the building is increased, producing greater strains on the foundations, which will need to be designed to cope with them. Third, this option is relatively costly when compared to that of using special insulation materials.

There are two basic methods of providing insulation. One includes placing the insulation material as an insert (like the filling of a sandwich) and the other is to integrate it into the envelope's component material. The first method is most common: examples include the use of pre-compressed polystyrene placed between profiled metal sheets, or of glass fibre quilting placed in timber framed panels. An example of the second method is the use of an insulation aggregate added to wall plaster or floor screed.

The contributing factors to the thermal efficiency of a building can be summarised as:

(a) exposure
(b) orientation
(c) shape and weight
(d) internal layout.

Exposure and orientation have already been discussed. Internal layout is important mainly in terms of the placement of heat sources and the relationship of internal spaces to external openings in the building shell. With regard to shape and weight, the smaller the external surface area of the building's walls and roofs, the less the heat loss. There is a directly proportional relationship between heat loss and area: *the greater the area, the greater the heat loss*. The ideal shape for minimal heat loss is the square. A rectangular building of the same floor area as a square building could have walls in the ratio of 1:3:1. This would give an increase of over 11% in total surface area when compared to the square building. This means, of course, 11% more shell to allow heat loss.

The weight of a building is also important in the context of its ability to respond to thermal inputs. A thick, solid wall, which could be of heavy mass, will respond much slower to thermal inputs than a thin cavity wall, which could be of lighter mass. The converse is also true: a heavyweight wall will give out its stored heat at a much slower rate than a lightweight wall. The type of wall used may, therefore, depend upon the use of the buildings and the need for internal heating. It might be better to use thermally heavyweight walls for buildings requiring continuous heating, which after initial slow warm up do not readily cool, while for those requiring instant or intermittent heat it might be better to use thermally lightweight walls.

P. Burberry in *Practical Thermal Design in Buildings* (Mitchell, 1983) has identified six major aspects which form the basis for strategic design decisions. Each will now be considered.

Location and siting

Geographical location will influence the number of degree-days. Exposure can cause high wind speeds which will increase both fabric and ventilation losses. The configuration of the ground is important: frost hollows, for example, can induce lower air temperatures than surrounding areas. Noise and air pollution may preclude the use of natural ventilation. In summer, mechanical ventilation may not be adequate, so expensive air conditioning may be required.

Environmental strategy

Decisions as to how the internal climate in the building is to be controlled or created must be included in the initial design appraisal. Will air conditioning be used? What is the method of space heating? How do these relate to the fenestration of the shell? What materials are available?

Building form

The following aspects must be considered: shape and topography of the site; town planning restrictions; space to allow insulation, daylight and ventilation; conformity with surrounding buildings; and different design approaches. Within the building, constraints can be imposed on natural lighting and ventilation, on the form of the building, and on the grouping of rooms based on function.

Internal planning

Large open areas are difficult to control. Air pressures are greatest at the external corners of buildings, where entrances ought not to be sited, therefore. Areas of similar internal temperature should be grouped together.

Zoning and fenestration

Zoning is the division of a building into areas where heat can be related to use. Service installations are normally zoned, but these may not coincide with the internal functional-use form of the building. It is necessary to match these to achieve energy savings. Fenestration ought to be designed in relation to the orientation of the façade (it may not be practical to have the same number, size, shape and type of window on all façades) and to the internal functions of rooms. The glazing should correspond with the zones.

Thermal response

This depends on the structure and materials of the shell. Whether to use heavyweight or lightweight thermal constructions must also be considered over the seasons. What about different parts of the building? Do they need to differ in construction detail to deal with varying heating requirements?

In constructing highly insulated shells a number of problems can arise, from the design itself, from moisture penetration, from poor ventilation and from construction detailing. All these factors could manifest themselves as condensation.

One effect of good thermal insulation is that the temperature of a building's cladding will be raised to that of the air temperature in hot weather, yet the heat falling on the surface will not penetrate and be dissipated within the fabric's structure. Although the insulation will keep heat out of the building (and in the winter keep it in) it can create large temperature differences between internal and external surfaces. This problem has already been alluded to in the discussion of material properties (pp.43–50).

External air humidity has little influence on internal condensation risk; it is the interior air humidity which can cause the problem. This humidity is generated by the occupants and their activities, together with any heating appliances based on gas or paraffin. These factors have not changed dramatically over the last few years, but the incidence of condensation in some form has increased in those buildings built since the early 1960s in the UK. The factors which have contributed to this condensation increase (which can produce mould growth) can be identified as follows:

(a) *Ventilation*. A relaxation in the regulations requiring ventilators to be placed in habitable rooms, together with changes in window design to improve airtightness (including the rejection of a small opening light for night ventilation), resulted in less ventilation to rooms.

(b) *Materials*. New building materials, such as sheet metals and plastics, concrete panels and, of course, the insulation material itself, have reduced the ability of building fabrics to absorb excess water vapour.

(c) The use of sophisticated space heating instead of open fires again did not allow the building's fabric to react significantly to heat. The open fire gave radiated heat which warmed internal surfaces; heating could not be easily switched off and so was provided over several hours and the brickwork surrounds gave off heat while cooling.

(d) Patterns of occupancy and operation have changed over the years. Many dwellings are empty during the day and heating is only switched on in the late afternoon and evening, and in the early morning. A greater use of hot water for baths, showers, washing-up and for washing machines has also increased the amount of water vapour present in the average home.

The UK government has stressed the need to reduce energy consumption in buildings, advocating such means as draught-proofing the jambs of doors and fixing draught-excluders to the bottoms of doors. These items further reduce natural ventilation, thereby increasing further the risk of condensation.

Condensation can manifest itself in two areas of a building's fabric: on wall, floor and ceiling surfaces, and within the fabric itself. In the first instance, it is usually visible; in the second it is commonly hidden, and termed *interstitial condensation* as it occurs in the spaces between elements of the wall, floor or roof. The problems caused by condensation will be explained later, in the discussion of deterioration (see p.75–116). Suffice it to say here that in designing the fabric the risk of condensation should be eliminated as far as possible. Plotting temperature gradients across a construction will show where condensation could occur. The use of materials with impervious surfaces can provide unwelcome areas for the deposition of water vapour. Questions must be asked: Where does this run to off the surface? Can it be prevented from condensing on the surface? Can some form of ventilation be created in enclosed spaces to reduce the risk of interstitial condensation but not reduce the benefits of added insulation?

The need to increase the amount of insulation within the pitched roof of a domestic dwelling (at ceiling level) in the UK has rendered the roof space a relatively cold area. Water vapour from the activities of the occupants rises to the roof space. This warmed air can penetrate into this space and meet with the colder air; condensation will take place and water will be deposited on the roof timbers. If the air is static it can create conditions ideal for fungal growth. To reduce this risk, permanent ventilators can be placed at eave level, together with vents at the ridge, allowing the free circulation of air to carry away the water vapour. Similar methods can be introduced into flat roof construction. It is more difficult to create a free flow of air within a wall construction, but one means adopted is to insert a water vapour barrier which prevents the vapour entering the unventilated core of the construction. It is ironic that in endeavouring to make improvements in the thermal resistance of the shell a major detrimental factor has arisen. Although this is now recognised, there are many buildings which will unfortunately show deterioration resulting from condensation due to the increased use of thermal insulation.

Much attention has been given to thermal analysis of materials of construction as if they have no thermal capacity at all, and as if any change in temperature, externally or internally, instantaneously affects all parts of the building. This does not happen in practice. The ability of materials to absorb heat is considerable and this will have a marked effect on performance. As it is now necessary to evaluate long-term energy-conserving performance it is essential to make allowance for thermal capacity. There are two ways in which thermal capacity can be taken into account in calculations. The first is by employing the mean temperature difference over a period of time, if this is known or can be estimated, which cancels out the effect of variations. The second way takes into account the actual performance of materials in absorbing heat. The former is known as the *seasonal heat requirement technique*, and the latter as the *admittance method*. In this latter method, the thermal conductivity and the thermal capacity of a material form a combined function known as *thermal diffusity*. As knowledge increases regarding the thermal behaviour of materials in construction, so this is found to be more complex. There is constant change due to variations in temperature, climatic conditions and heat inputs and outputs; all these factors create a dynamic solution. As calculations become more complicated, so computers are used to model the circumstances. These can give clear and accurate information on the behaviour of walls, roofs, floors, etc.

SOUND INSULATION

The growing importance of creating a barrier against sound, whether from a source within or without a building, is engaging both designers and builders. Noise is a major contribution to the stress suffered by urban dwellers and workers. The importance of a consideration of noise in the design of the climatic barrier is summed up in the following statement from Croome, D.J., *Noise, buildings and people* (Pergamon Press, 1977):

A building structure creates a modified climate for its people; its material controls the interchange of light, heat, solar radiation, moisture, ions and noise between the external and internal environments. Building shape and form not only control the passage of wind, smoke and noise around buildings but they also control the spatial/temporal patterns of sound, light and air movement inside the building.

The factors that need to be considered in the control of noise in buildings, especially the shell, are listed in Fig. 1.6.

comfort
physical & subjective qualities & quantities
                                in acoustics
quality of life : understanding stress
noise and people : physiological response
                        noise and sleep
                            noise criteria in the future
effect of noise on human performance
noise and speech communication

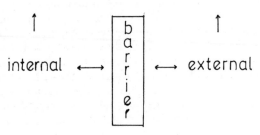

Fig. 1.6   *Factors in the control of noise*

Comfort

To be subjected to unwanted noise is at the very least uncomfortable, and can be extremely annoying. Even if the sound is the relatively pleasant one of music, musical tastes differ! Research has shown that noise can be a potent factor in the production and exacerbation of stress. It can affect the quality of sleep and attitudes to neighbours and to the district lived in. Even the noise of one's own children can be stressful. The perception of noise is determined by the environment, by the task being performed and by the internal human state, including level of anxiety, drowsiness, and the effects of alcohol or drugs.

What is comfort? Comfort is governed by four factors: *arousal level*; *physical sensation level*; *emotional sensation level*; and *distraction level*. These in combination will determine the levels of comfort perceived by an individual and will vary from person to person. Croome has postulated a comfort model based on the above four factors and these are affected by a whole host of other factors including work task, personal susceptibility to environment, physical sensitivity, emotional sensitivity, intelligence, concentration ability, past experience of event, expectance, quality of stimulus, information, content of stimulus, and interaction with other factors.

Physical and subjective qualities and acoustics

The loudness of noise is to be taken into account, together with its pitch and timbre. Various combinations at different levels will alter the perception of the noise.

Quality of life: understanding stress

Individuals vary widely in their reactions to stress. For example, introverts tend to seek peace and quiet, favour solitude or restricted companionship, and are often sensitive, restrained and self-driving, whereas extroverts often enjoy noisier environments, more social contacts and tend to be less restrained and less self-driving. Stress is imposed on individuals by the world about them and produces a degree of strain in the individual. The stress-strain pattern will depend on the psychological and physiological make-up of the individual and will show short-term and long-term variations.

Noise and people

Noise is gathered and sensed via the ear and if this mechanism is damaged, either by excessive noise levels or by disease, then hearing can be impaired. Most people live and work in environments with noise levels of less than 85 decibels, which is where risk of damage is thought to start. There is much research being carried out at present to give an understanding of the effect noise has on people, but there is no disagreement that long and loud noise *does* affect the ear and can lead to stress and strain.

It has been found that sleep is best enjoyed at levels of less than 35dB(A). It is likely that as the effects of noise become more understood then levels of loudness, pitch and timbre may be determined for particular environments. At present, different nations have different values which they deem to be acceptable for various environments such as workplaces, the home, and shops and recreation areas. It is likely that the international range of values will contract, and therefore in some nations increased standards of sound insulation may need to be introduced.

Effect of noise on human performance

Research has shown that the performance of complex tasks deteriorates in noisy environments, i.e. above 100 decibels. The number of errors increased, but speed of working and response time remained unaffected. Noise in the range 64–95 decibels can improve the performance of simple work tasks, i.e. those with a low rate of information input.

Little research has been carried out on the various combinations of noise, heat and light acting together on an individual. If the behaviour of people in an environment is not known, however, it is difficult for designers and builders to provide a building shell which will satisfactorily create a comfortable space with the minimum of stress factors. More research and investigation therefore needs to be carried out to ensure that the right performance standards are being set before designers and builders specify the appropriate constructions.

Noise and speech communication

In spaces where speech is the primary mode of communication it is important that the reverberant conditions, the background sound levels, and the positions of speaker and listeners allow the speech to be clearly understood. The words spoken must be intelligible to an audience which may have a wide range of 'hearing efficiencies'. The climatic barrier can influence the background sound levels and the reverberant conditions.

NOISE SOURCES

Noise can be generated internally by air flow systems, water flow systems, air conditioning and heating systems, machines, type-writers, lifts and voices. External noise is generated mainly by road traffic, but can also include air traffic, voices, and 'noise escape' from other buildings.

The role of the building shell in protecting against external noise

Our concern here is with the acoustic pathway between the inner and outer environments of a building. The main point in the selection of building fabrics is an optimisation of several factors, of which sound insulation is one. In any building the weakest sound barriers are glazed areas and doorways. Secondary sound transmission pathways can exist via fresh air intakes, exhaust outlets or chimneys. The quality of construction, as, for example, where there is an inefficient closing of joints, can affect the passage of sound by providing further pathways.

Windows provide a model upon which acoustic factors can be described with relation to the building's envelope. The acoustical performance factors are as follows:

(a) *Weight*. Weight depends on the thickness of the glass: 4–6mm is the norm; if the thickness is increased to 12mm only a further 2 decibel reduction will be gained.

(b) *Cavity width*. To achieve some gain in sound insulation a minimum width of 100mm is required, but ideally it should be 2–300mm. This compares with 15mm for optimum thermal transfer reduction.

(c) *Absorbent linings*. The air space forms a resonant cavity; a 25mm lining will increase the mean insulation value by about 2 decibels due to absorption of the reverberant field energy in the cavity.

(d) *Damping*. The vibration of the glass panes can be minimised by using framed rubber gaskets. Other methods include the use of laminated glass with resilient inter-layers; the use of differing glass thickness in each pane to avoid coincidence frequency matching; and the use of non-parallel panes.

(e) *Mechanical separation*. Panes should be isolated from each other and the opening in the structure housing the frames should not be bridged. Separate frames are preferable to one common frame.

(f) *Sealing*. Sealing is one of the most important factors in the acoustical design of windows. Gaps most commonly occur between the glass and the opening frame, and between the sub-frame and the wall opening. These gaps may be caused by incorrect tolerances, poor workmanship, thermal stresses, structural movement or material deterioration (perhaps due to insufficient maintenance).

(g) *Size and shape of glass*. As the size of a pane decreases, the transmission loss in the coincidence region is improved, whereas the resonance frequency is increased.

(h) *Edge fixing*. Sound incidence upon the glass pane causes it to bend. The bending wave is reflected at the edge to form a flexual wave which at and above the critical frequency causes a large increase in the sound radiated from the pane. If the edge of the glass is clamped between hardwood beads or neoprene strips, or suspended in mastic, then the flexural wave energy is attenuated by absorption and reflection at the mounting.

To obtain a high degree of sound insulation, all the above factors will need to be considered in the window design. A major point to be noted is that good sound insulation cannot be obtained by single glazing, even it if is 12mm thick. The next most important factor is that related to the fixing of the window. Unless this is carried out to the highest standards of workmanship any design characteristics will be circumvented. The builder's role in forming a climatic barrier is paramount and should not be underestimated. The science of the design may lie outside the scope of the builder's responsibilities, but knowledge of the factors used in design should be known to enable the appropriate procedure to occur on site.

Further protections from external noise

One way in which external noise can be reduced is by stifling it at source, or by totally preventing its propagation. In the UK a number of Acts of Parliament have been passed controlling the incidence of noise where it can be classified as a 'nuisance' as with a loud radio or a particularly noisy factory. Car manufacturers and motorcycle riders have to provide suitable silencers for combustion engines. One selling point in the marketing of a modern car is the quietness of its engine, from both inside and outside the vehicle. A problem remains with large lorries, which not only create a relatively loud noise but also emit sound frequencies which can contribute to the deterioration of a building by literally buffeting its structure. While technology can provide good levels of sound reduction, the social concern to provide a quieter environment will bring pressure to reduce the noise at source.

Road traffic noise can be abated by considering one or a combination of the following factors:

(a) *Distance*. The further the building from the traffic, the less the noise.
(b) *Building orientation*. If openings and areas of low sound insulation are placed away from the sources then its effect will be reduced.
(c) *Noise screens*. Walls, trees and banks of earth can be incorporated into landscape designs to prevent noise penetration. These screens need to be long, to prevent the noise flanking around the ends of the barrier.
(d) *Façade materials*. The materials and types of façade constructions, together with the total areas of glazing, will affect the amount of noise penetrating into a building.

The BRE suggests that the basis for evaluating noise from traffic should be an 18–hour criterion. This is defined as the hourly value of the noise level in dB (A) measured at a distance of 1 metre from the relevant face of the building that is exceeded for 10% or more of the hours between 6 a.m. and midnight on a normal weekday. The average values set for the 18-hour criterion are:

Offices and commercial buildings   77dB
Residential buildings   68dB

Noise generated within a building can affect two groups of people: those within and those outside. Of the climatic conditions noise is the only one which requires a measure of technological activity in order to reduce its impact, not only on the building envelope but also on the internal structure itself, from floor to floor and from room to room. Noise here is loosely considered as a climatic condition, although invariably it is manufactured by man and is not a natural occurrence. A few observations will illustrate its importance in the design of a climatic barrier.

Protection from internal noise

As stated earlier, one way to reduce the need for sound insulation is to inhibit the noise at source. If this is generated from within a building then technology should be used to combat its propagation. For example, the use of a floating floor can reduce the transmission of noise from one level to another within a building, thereby constraining its propagation to the space immediately around its source. Walls can be sound-proofed, and a system of sound lobbies with sound-proofed doors can be installed to protect against high noise levels. If the sound-proofed wall is on the perimeter of a building then the noise is prevented from travelling out to create problems for people in adjoining buildings, and the ingress of externally created noise is also obstructed. If the noise source is confined within the building, its level must be within bounds acceptable to those people working in it. A building with a number of separate users (a block of flats, for example) must shield each user from the possible noise of the others. In new building design this can be achieved relatively easily, but problems arise where a building is undergoing refurbishment or a change of use. The physical problems involved in introducing sound-proofing to existing walls and floors are many, and although they can be overcome they are expensive. For example, to sound-proof a timber floor involves taking up the floorboards, laying resilient quilt and some form of pugging between the joists (if the ceiling can stand the weight) and relaying the boarding. Walls need to have an extra layer of sound absorbent material applied to their surfaces, or to be completely rebuilt. This might result in a loss of floor area. The nature of the sound needs to be considered, whether it is airborne or carried by the structure. It may travel through the structure because it derives from the impact of machine vibrations. Or it may be primarily airborne, deriving from the clatter of working parts.

Sound insulation is largely an interplay between mass, stiffness and damping and the designer has to match these in relation to the type of sound and the function of the building element, be it wall, roof or floor. Good sound insulation is usually a combination of low stiffness, high mass and high damping, achieved within cost constraints.

Planning for sound insulation

Figure 1.7 shows the basic processes involved in planning for sound insulation. Before any insulation measures can be determined it is necessary to discover the characteristics of the external noise climate. Such aspects as loudness, frequency, timing, source, type of noise, need to be ascertained. The basic philosophy of the architecture needs to be clarified. This involves not only a consideration of style and aesthetics, but also of the process of design. For example, is the building made up of prefabricated components? Has it a flexible steel frame, or is it constructed of

assess external noise climate
design criteria/approach for building
sound reduction index for envelope
orientation of the building
sound reduction index for internal walls, doors, ceilings and floors
amount of absorption material
assess acoustical performance of all equipment to be used in the building

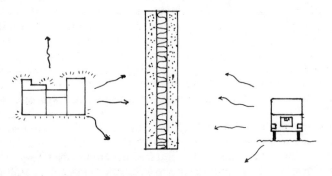

Fig. 1.7   *Planning for sound insulation*

load-bearing brickwork? Is it designed with a low energy usage in mind?

Following directly upon the external noise assessment is the decision on the sound reduction required for the envelope. This will be governed by the needs of its users, together with a consideration of the external environment.   ·

Those rooms which house activities especially sensitive to noise need to be furthest from its source. The building will need to be orientated to accommodate this factor. Internally, a sound reduction index will have to be determined. This may vary from room to room or from floor to floor depending upon use of the room. It will also vary according to proximity to unwelcome internal and external noise sources.

The type and amount of absorption material will depend upon the chosen structure of the walls, floors and roof. It will need to complement the architectural style and be easily integrated into the structure. Its cost will have to be offset against other elemental costs and weighed against the predicted benefits for the users.

Finally, the acoustic performance of the equipment in the building must be assessed to foresee its impact on the users and upon those people outside. Some revisions of the foregoing procedures may be required to match the need to control both internal and external noise.

It can be seen from this brief discussion of noise and the building that there are many aspects that need to be taken into account. From time to time papers are published, by the BRE, by British Standards and in the form of codes of practice, which give information on the current state of research and development. With the present demand for indoor leisure facilities such as entertainment auditoria and convention centres, there is a growing wealth of specialist knowledge on sound and its propagation and control. The discerning architect or builder will employ this knowledge in providing more comfortable buildings for all activities.

FIRE INSULATION

The function of fire insulation in the envelope is indirectly connected to the envelope's general performance as a climatic barrier. The need to provide fire resistant measures can affect the shell's ability to provide the other functions listed in Fig. 3.1 (p.119). As this topic is discussed in some detail in Part Three of this volume, only some general introductory remarks will be made here in relation to its integration into the climatic barrier.

The desired levels of fire resistance can be achieved in a number of ways: (a) by the use of incombustible materials for the construction of the façade; (b) by using materials of limited combustibility to give fire resistance for a notional time period; (c) by giving some form of protection to the basic components of the shell by providing a protective coating; and (d) by using liquid in the structural components of the envelope as a heat dissipator.

Some materials, such as brick and concrete, have an inbuilt resistance to fire as well as a capacity to satisfy the other major functions for good climatic performance. In both materials, thickness will determine the standards of performance: the greater the thickness, the greater the ability to resist the vagaries of the weather and the effects of fire. In the case of concrete, the correct cover to the reinforcement has to be ensured. Materials such as steel need added protection to give the required fire resistance, and the type of protection used may alter its ability to withstand the general effects of the weather.

An optimum solution would be to use a material on a façade or roof construction which would satisfy fire resistance and all other requirements without either added protection or further treatment. Brick and concrete can do this for a façade, but the roof poses greater problems. Fire technology will be discussed later (see pp.117–76).

ILLUMINATION

The great majority of buildings have a need for natural lighting. There is a fundamental psychological need for human beings to have sight of some aspect of the external environment. Although this may not be consciously expressed during the course of a normal working day, if the majority of people were deprived of natural light a reaction would soon be forthcoming.

The diffusion of the sun's rays through the sky means that the whole sky becomes luminous. The level of daylight available from this luminosity is usually expressed in terms of the total illuminance received on an unobstructed horizontal plane. This is predictable in the case of direct sunlight to within quite close limits and depends principally upon the sun's position and the clarity of the atmosphere. When the sky is partly or wholly cloud-covered the level of available sky-light can vary widely.

Daylight design is usually based on the selection of a level of sky-light which will be available as a minimum, with some specified frequency, such as 90% of all working hours. It is conventional in most countries outside the USA to express the level of sky-light illuminance within buildings in terms of the *daylight factor*, defined as 'the ratio of the daylight illuminance at a point on a given plane due to the light received directly or indirectly from a sky of assumed or known illuminance distribution, to the illuminance on a horizontal plane due to an unobstructed hemisphere of this sky.' Direct sunlight is excluded from both values of illuminance.

The horizontal plane is usually taken at table level, but the daylight factor can also be applied to any sloping or vertical plane. The usual practice is to determine values at a number of reference points within the room of interest. If these values are then multiplied by an appropriate figure of total external illuminance, the results are the anticipated illuminances at the points.

In order to design for daylight the following process is commonly adopted.

(a) From an appropriate Lighting Code select the recommended illuminance level for the type of building and visual task.
(b) Determine the value for the 'design sky' in terms of the total external illuminance available for some percentage of working hours.
(c) Determine the resulting required daylight factor.
(d) After making allowances for dirt on glass, obstruction by window framing, etc., select an arrangement of windows or roof-lights which will produce the required daylight factor.

The key factor in this procedure is the selection of a value for the 'design sky'. In the UK a standard overcast sky providing an outdoor illuminance of 5000 lux is used, representing average conditions in England over the greater part of winter days, over long periods in later autumn, and early and on wet days in summer. In practice this means that most buildings cannot be adequately lit by daylight alone.

It is generally accepted that direct sunlight should be excluded from working areas because of the intolerable glare which might arise. There is also a separate but further effect from direct sunlight: that of unwanted thermal gain. In order for sunlight to augment sky-light the building's façade must be designed to redirect the sun's rays, on to a white ceiling, for example. Special ventilation blinds can also be used. In order to bring daylight into the middle and lower regions of the Hong Kong and Shanghai Bank Building in Hong Kong, a system of lenses have been used. These move round following the path of the sun automatically, thereby continuously redirecting the light.

The path of the sun can be calculated using specially prepared diagrams. Alternatively, computer programs can simulate the effect of the sun on a building, in all its facets and for all times of the year, with the building located at its latitude and longitude. By using three dimensional modelling the exact effect of daylight (and sunlight) can be projected into a space within the building. The shape and size of the windows can then be correspondingly adjusted.

In areas of the world where sunlight is strong, the façade will have to be designed to protect against effects such as glare and thermal gain. The development of the so-called 'smart skins' for building envelopes attempts to control automatically these effects by using materials such as electrochromic glass.

Where roof-lighting can be used, three main forms exist: (a) saw tooth glazing; (b) monitors with veritcal or sloping glass; and (c) flat or low pitched roofs with glazing incorporated into the roofing surface (obviously, this can only be used on single storey buildings or on the upper levels of multi-storey buildings).

It is difficult to use side windows to provide satisfactory day-light. While the light might be adequate near to the windows, its intensity will fall off rapidly towards the back of the room. As a general guide, satisfactory daylighting can be provided in rooms only where the distance to the rear of the room does not exceed three times the window height, provided that free access for light is possible from outside.

VENTILATION

In the quest to create a building shell as an effective climatic barrier, ventilation has been drastically reduced. Unwanted draughts have all but been eliminated and with the need to conserve energy (in the provision of space heating) air flow within and consequently out of the building have been reduced. When coal fires were common, natural ventilation was obtained via the chimney. Many domestic dwellings were designed and built with permanent vents in the form of air bricks to the outside. In addition, where suspended timber floors were used, underfloor ventilation was provided. Doors and windows also allowed some ventilation due to shrinkage and wear and tear.

Of course, the comfort of people within a draughty building is poor compared to a non-draughty space, but, as a consequence of reducing the number of air vents, health problems can arise. Already mentioned in this chapter is the problem of condensation. Its degree of effect upon the internal atmosphere is governed by the rate of air changes. Generally, the greater the number of air changes the less the chance of condensation. To produce the required air changes, many commercial and public buildings use some form of mechanical ventilation, or air conditioning.

Building envelopes are now constructed as virtually airtight skins with no manual ventilation facilities. Lobbies are formed at entrances to prevent excess air flow, windows cannot be opened and the internal environment is controlled totally. In the case of relatively simple mechanical ventilation, outlets need to be provided in the building's envelope to allow the air to be exhausted. Two problems need to be overcome: first, that of blending the ventilation outlets into the aesthetic design of the building, and, second, that of ensuring that the outlets do not weaken the other functional elements of the façade or roof. Where there is a protrusion through an external surface, weather-tightness, the existence of thermal bridges and the effect on fire resistance need to be assessed.

In the calculation of energy demands and targets for the design of new buildings and services the CIBSE (Chartered Institution of Building Services Engineers) Building Energy Code gives the following information:

The ventilation heat loss rate, nv3, is calculated from the mean natural ventilation rate in air changes per hour over 24 hours, 'n', and the volume of the heated space, 'v'. For naturally ventilated buildings the value of n is assessed to be constant and, in calculations for peripheral strips up to 7.5m in depth, it should be taken as unit, but elsewhere, in the core of the building, no allowance for natural infiltration should be made. For educational buildings, a fresh air ventilation rate of at least $30m^3/h$ for each person should be allowed.

As the heat loss through ventilation is only calculated around the internal periphery of the building it is recognised that the envelope cannot be completely sealed and that some air movement will take place. Elsewhere, the Code makes further comments with respect to ventilation. Each air supply system should be designed to use up to and including 100% of the system capacity for cooling with outdoor air automatically, whenever its use will result in lower use of energy. Outdoor air should not be provided to occupied buildings other than for combustion or any other essential purposes or where an overall energy saving can be shown and, whenever possible, the system and its controls should be arranged accordingly. Where mechanically ventilated buildings are likely to be only partially occupied, the possibility of designing the installation to incorporate multiple ventilation systems should be considered. Separate systems can then serve discrete areas and those not required may be shut off. This may mean a greater number of inlets and outlets, with a consequent effect on the integrity of the building's envelope.

Scholsty and Williams, in *The Builder's Guide to Solar Construction* (McGraw-Hill, 1982) have put forward the concept of the 'tight' building shell. As the need for more control over the internal environment increases it is necessary to construct a shell which can perform according to specification. It cannot be allowed to 'leak' unaccountably as this will disrupt the internal climate. The air ventilation must be forecast and accounted for in the calculations for heat loss, etc. It is likely that a greater range of buildings will be built under this principle and that adequate ventilation will become a major mechanical design consideration.

The above trend does bring into question the effects this may have on the building's occupants' health. Concern has been shown, reinforced by research evidence, that the incidence of some complaints such as headaches, asthma and legionella is greater in buildings relying upon mechanical ventilation and air conditioning systems. This is known as the 'sick building syndrome' (see Finnegan, M.J., Pickering, C.A.C. and Burge, P., *The Sick Building Syndrome: prevalence studies*, British Medical Journal, 1984 , 289(2) 8 Dec.: 1573–1575). Research has found that six medical symptoms are consistently and significantly more prevalent among workers in sealed, air conditioned buildings, compared with those in naturally ventilated buildings. The symptoms are all non-specific and could occur commonly within the general population, depending upon personal susceptibility. The six symptoms are: (a) runny, itchy or blocked nose; (b) dry throat; (c) eye irritation; (d) headache; (e) lethargy; and (f) dry skin. Not only were the six symptoms significantly more prevalent in sealed buildings, but no other work-related symptoms of similar frequency were volunteered during the study. This indicates that the 'sick building syndrome' is not merely a chance collection of symptoms but a phenomenon connected to a building itself. What causes these symptoms? Investigation is continuing and is so far inconclusive, but contributory factors may include: (a) pollutants in the air (from internal or external sources); (b) environmental design factors such as thermal climate, fluorescent lighting, air speed and humidity; and (c) an excess of positive ions. Research will need to relate symptoms to manipulations of the internal environment. As yet there is no hard information on the symptom prevalence levels at which a building becomes 'sick' (that is, when remedial action is required), nor on how many buildings are 'sick'. At the very least a 'sick building' can seriously affect the productivity of the workforce and in one documented case the sickness absence rate rose by 30% in the first year.

Another pollutant which is proving a major problem in penetrating the building's envelope is radon. This is a natural radioactive gas, a decay product of radium which is created in the ground. It gains entry to the building by air seeping through the ground floor and through gaps at floor edges or elsewhere (through drains or inlet ducts for example). As buildings normally exhibit a slight negative air pressure relative to the external environment, the gas can be drawn in. Abnormally high doses of radon can significantly increase the risk of lung cancer. The phenomenon occurs in certain parts of the UK. Measures should be developed to prevent its ingress into buildings.

CLIMATIC BARRIER AS INTERFACE

To recapitulate, the factors presented in Fig. 1.4 (energy, materials, components, design, maintenance, cost and function) have been introduced. It is the interrelationship of all these factors which produces the climatic barrier and acts as an interface between internal and external environments. Can these factors be given a ranking? Is there a procedure for determining the optimum building shell? In precise terms the answer is 'No', but there are some guiding principles and systems being developed which attempt to utilise scientific knowledge to design and build envelopes which will satisfy performance criteria.

The initial performance criteria must be centred on those listed under *function*. The shell must be capable of performing to all the individual functions, which are based on data and information gathered regarding the local climate. These functions must be directly related to the prevailing weather conditions. Brought into this band of functions is the concern for *energy*, its consumption and conservation, and the use of natural sources. The *design approach* will influence how the question of energy is related to function. Must the façade contain the heat produced within the building? Can solar heating be utilised in supplementing the space heating requirements? Can the adoption of a particular shape, volume and layout reduce energy consumption? Can the fabric be designed to recirculate internal heat? To what extent will the scope of *maintenance* activities involve the use of energy? Will deterioration affect the performance as regards function and use of energy? It is not until questions such as these have been answered that decisions on *materials*, *components* and other production details can begin to be formulated. These decisions will be governed by *cost*, although initial cost is but one aspect of the total costs attributable to a building's envelope. Techniques such as 'life cycle costing' can give guidance on the total costs relating to different constructional solutions. In the final analysis trade-offs between all the factors need to be made. These can occur between each of the functions and between some or all of the factors shown in Fig. 3.1 (p.119).

The development work undertaken by Radford and Gero is relevant here (see Radford, A.D. and Gero, J.S., 'Trade-off diagrams for the integrated design of the physical environment in buildings' in *Solar energy applications in the design of buildings*, edited by Cowan, H.J., Applied Science Publishers Ltd., 1980). Although their work is confined to a small number of physical functions, the principles expounded can be applied to other physical functions, together with factors such as cost, energy, use, etc. Their thesis is centred on the assumption that rational design is based on information, but that most of this information comes from manuals, codes and simplified mathematical models, and that there is a separation between the design roles of the architect and the services engineer. This separation has not aided the efficient design of internal environments. Simulation techniques based on computer programs exist, but their disadvantage is that they require the user to operate by trial and error. To obtain any quantitative information the architect must first have a solution, and so the design process becomes a cycle of postulation, evaluation and modification in progressively finer detail.

There is also a need for information about the relationship between different environmental components. In designing a building the designer's concern is to find the solution, taken as a whole, that is the best that can be devised. In environmental design this requires some form of prescriptive quantitative information which relates the performances achievable for different environmental attributes not only to the building design but also to each other. The following example describes the implications of choosing a certain level of performance in one environmental attribute for the performance that can be achieved in some other attribute, by quantifying the trade-offs involved.

Take a room for which natural lighting is required without a need for air-conditioning in summer. Here, two environmental attributes are of prime interest: *natural lighting* and *summer thermal conditions*. In order to make a comparison of the design solution's performance the attributes must be interpreted in terms of measurable criteria. Suitable criteria would include the daylight factor at the rear of the room in overcast sky conditions, and the peak internal environment temperature in predicted external conditions at the height of summer. Different design solutions have the potential to provide an infinite number of different feasible combinations of predicted daylight factors and peak temperatures. The feasible combinations will be restricted by the range of feasible values of the design variables, and the physical laws which determine the relationship between internal and external conditions. If the feasible combinations were plotted on a graph, with daylight factor against peak temperature, they would lie within an envelope. There would also be a maximum possible value for daylight for any specific value of peak temperature. The designer will be interested to know how much worsening of thermal performance must be accepted for a bettering of daylight performance. The design options can be made clear if the set of performance combinations can be identified, such that improved levels of daylight factor are always obtained at a minimum disadvantage in terms of peak temperature.

A system model has been developed which takes into account a comprehensive set of design variables, such as the detailing of internal and external walls, floors, ceilings and surfaces, and the position and projection of continuous horizontal and vertical sun-shades. The model must be employed at the level of the individual room or area. To take the case of an external wall, this can be divided into a number of sub-planes. Windows, solid and open areas will be made up of numbers of these sub-planes, and sun-shades will be positioned on this grid. The effect of a particular location on the internal environment will be determined by the degree to which the external environment (solar radiation, external temperature, noise levels, etc.) impinges upon it, and by the properties of the construction form which occupies it. It would be impractical for every location to be occupied by a different construction form, even if that situation resulted in good environmental performance. There will be practical restrictions on the way materials fit together to produce a feasible solution.

An architect or designer will also have specific ideas about the form of the envelope design with regard to aesthetics. These requirements are modelled by a set of design rules which can be nominated by the architect or designer, which will therefore limit the space available for the solution. The greater the design restrictions, the less the computation. The design rules are grouped under three classes of constraint:

(a) Topology: restrictions on the number and spatial relation of windows and other elements.
(b) Geometry: restrictions on the position, shape and minimum, and maximum lengths and heights of an element.
(c) Materials: restrictions on acceptable forms of construction, the number of different materials and the points at which materials can change.

For the simplest model, the two criteria applied to the room are *daylight factor* and *peak summer internal environmental temperature*. In this case, the design variables to be taken into account are: (a) external wall construction types; (b) glass types; (c) window positions, heights and widths; and (d) horizontal sun shades. Up to three types of external wall construction and three types of glass are allowed, with the internal wall, floor and ceiling constructions remaining constant. Using this data a graphic trade-off curve can be produced which will relate daylight performance to peak internal environmental temperature. The qualitative performance information is provided by the length and shape of the trade-off curve. Quantitative information on performance is provided by reference to the axes of the graphs. Quantitative information on solutions concerns the actual sizes, positions and construction forms which result in optimal performance combinations in the various regions of the trade-off curve. The intention of the trade-off diagrams is to indicate design trends and directions rather than specific solutions. An example of trade-off curves is given in Fig. 1.8.

More complex situations can also be analysed by using the trade-off curve, including information on the orientation of rooms or obstruction from adjacent buildings, while employing the same basic physical criteria. A third criterion, such as *winter thermal performance*, can be introduced. The trade-off curves here will become three dimensional (creating surfaces) rather than two dimensional. The use of trade-off diagrams will identify the real design options for any situation. The main disadvantage with this technique, however, is the need to express performance in each environmental attribute in the form of a single-value criterion which is inherent in any use of optimisation. The choice of environmental components to be taken into account is left to the user, and may include trade-offs between winter and summer thermal performances, between day-lighting and noise intrusion, or between three or more of these environmental components at once. Different external conditions can be examined for their effect: for example, completely overcast skies with little solar radiation may be compared with clear skies with high solar radiation. To generate this data computer programs are available which use dynamic modelling for predicting the performance of the building's envelope and internal environment with respect to the climate.

These models attempt to represent the dynamics of the internal environment as it occurs within particular buildings and in particular climatic conditions. They can also give a clearer picture of what actually happens in heating/cooling cycles over a period of time. The first generation of computer-based models was based on handbooks, employing an analytical approach which was both simplified and piecemeal. A second generation realised the importance of dynamics but remained piecemeal and analytical, and as such is suitable only for low-order problems with time invariance. A third generation is now being developed which commences with a field problem approach, based on numerical methods which simulate an integrated view of energy sub-systems. Such models are suitable for high-order problems with time variations; they can consider heat and mass transfer, and be used more easily, often in association with computer-aided design systems.

An energy sub-system is a complex matrix of many factors, including *building orientation*, *wall construction*, *venting*, *infiltration*, *air movement*, and the *time dependence of users*. The building, its plant, machinery and control elements can be viewed as regions of greatly different time constants, having complex spatial and temporal relationships. Superimposed upon these are the time-dependent flow paths. The modelling techniques used

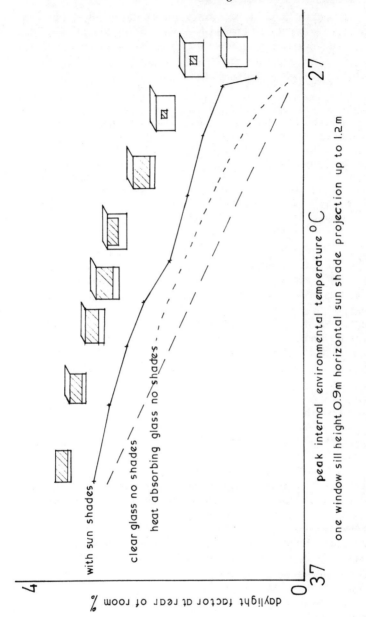

Fig. 1.8   *Trade-off curves (from Radford and Gero)*

must respect the laws of thermodynamics and causality, therefore.

With the current trend towards 'smart' or 'intelligent' buildings, the use of computer programs for thermal modelling will increase. Dr J.A. Clarke, in his report *The Future of Building Energy Modelling in the UK*, foresees that:

with the advent of powerful integrated computer-aided building design (CABD) systems, and considering the investment required to create and maintain the building description and to generate the related performance database, that practice will seek to evolve the computer-based model through the design process and beyond construction. One possible scenario is that a client of the future will expect delivery of a computer-based model and its performance database, in addition to the product of the design, the building. The information regarding building performance is then readily available for inspection. And the model itself can be used as the basis of intelligent control systems, trouble-shooting exercises, and retrofits.

The development of such programs is being carried out in conjunction with commercial computer research at such places as Cranfield Institute of Technology and the University of Strathclyde, Glasgow. Already, some 'intelligent' buildings have been designed and built and these are able to automatically control the internal environments according to the use patterns and the external climate with the prime concern of making efficient use of energy. The building envelope is both a barrier and an interface: it both withstands and creates climates.

QUESTIONS

1. Discuss the feasibility of meeting the various functional requirements of the building envelope, giving reasons for any order of priority amongst them.
2. Discuss how workmanship could affect a climatic barrier.
3. To what extent should the building fabric act as conserver of energy as compared to the capacity and range of internal services?
4. Discuss the implications for building technology if a greater emphasis is placed on the control of noise entering and leaving a building.
5. 'Natural lighting should be employed wherever possible.' Discuss this statement with respect to its effect on a building's envelope.
6. Investigate the use of computer programs as tools for modelling the internal climates of buildings.
7. Is the concept of 'intelligent' buildings only applicable to innovatory, prestigious buildings, or could it be applied to domestic housing?

Part Two
BUILDING DETERIORATION

4. Introduction

AGENCIES OF DETERIORATION

The deterioration of buildings is primarily caused by climatic conditions, but there are other contributory factors. Buildings not only deteriorate from the outside in, but also from the inside out. So far we have been concerned with the effects of climate and the ways in which the external envelope can cope with and modify climate. In this part the problem of degradation and decay will be examined in all its aspects, as listed in Fig. 2.1.

Climate

Enough has already been said about climate and its effect on a building, and the factors discussed hold good as major contributors to the deterioration of a building, primarily affecting its fabric. When the fabric fails, ingress occurs, and this can rapidly affect the internal structure and fabric. A good example is a leaking roof which allows water to penetrate into and through the ceiling zone, causing – at the very least – damp patches on the ceiling and adjoining walls, and staining of the decorations. At its worst it can promote structural failure by inducing corrosion or fungal attack on the roof components.

Pollution

In urban industrial environments a great number of waste products escape into the atmosphere. These may directly affect local buildings, as well as others some distance away if pollutants are

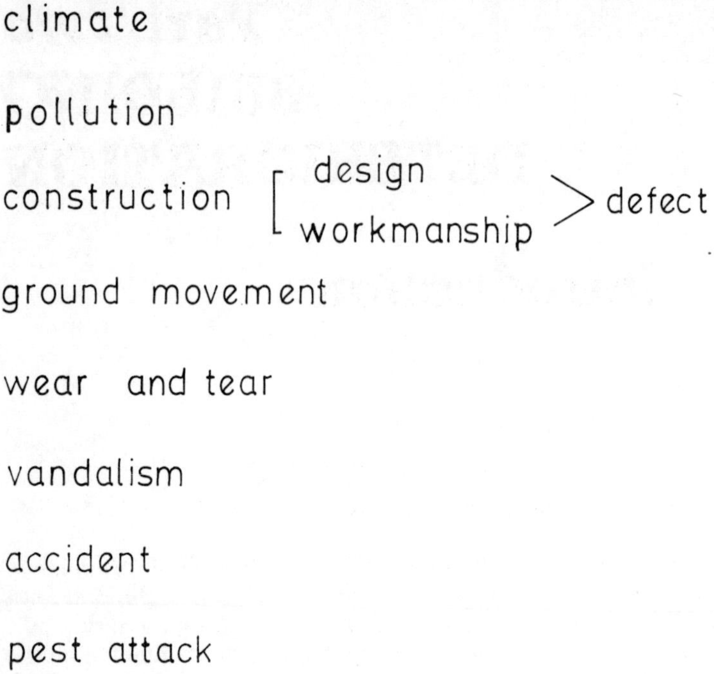

climate

pollution

construction ⌈ design
          ⌊ workmanship >defect

ground movement

wear and tear

vandalism

accident

pest attack

Fig. 2.1   *Agencies of deterioration*

carried up and away by wind. The effects of this type of pollution can be seen in staining on façades and the erosion of materials such as stone. As yet there is little definite knowledge of what chemicals or waste products do the most damage, whether vehicle exhaust fumes or emissions from electricity power plants.

Unfortunately, a building's owner cannot do much to prevent pollution problems as such sources are beyond his control. Pollution is not always apparent before construction, and it often manifests itself over a long period of time, causing gradual deterioration. The only effective way to reduce the problem is to eliminate the pollution at source. Experience has shown that industrialists are reluctant to do this voluntarily, so legislation such as the Clean Air Act in the UK has had to be passed through Parliament. There is much public concern over pollution affecting forests and woods in many European countries, including the UK. There is probably as much time, money and effort being spent by building owners on remedial work as there is just concern by environmentalists over the conservation of natural resources.

Indirectly, the building process itself can contribute to overall pollution problems in that the increasing use of oil fuels is concomitant with the increase of mechanisation on site. This is especially so in the case of earth- and materials-moving machinery, such as diggers, fork lift trucks and dumpers. Electric powered tools and machines do not produce waste products, but at present the use of electricity is restricted, due to the need for a supply to be delivered by cable. The power obtained from batteries is not sufficient to run large plant items nor to be effective over a working day. It is possible that batteries of sufficient capacity will be developed, which will reduce the need for plant run by combustion engines.

Construction form

If a building is not designed correctly, or is put together in a careless manner, any tendency towards deterioration will be accelerated. Inadequate materials may have been specified which are unsuitable for the environment. Joints between components may have been poorly sealed. Both inadequacies can lead to defects which will allow the climate to penetrate the fabric, and pollution to affect the façade; wear and tear may be accelerated and vandalism encouraged. The topic of construction form is important, and will be fully considered in Chapter 3.

Ground movement

Ground movement can cause a building to settle differentially, thereby producing cracks or even collapse. The cracks may be superficial and small, but if numerous and in a porous material they will lead to accelerated deterioration. Major cracks can allow the ingress or water and cold air in adverse weather, and therefore affect the internal environment.

There are many reasons for ground movement, including expansion/contraction of the sub-soil, erosion caused by flowing water, and a building mass too great for the bearing capacity, but the ultimate effect on the structure and fabric will be the same. Twisting or distortion of components can allow joints to open up. Stress and strain in metal structures or units can allow stress corrosion to occur. Settlement can literally break items, which in turn can lead to deterioration in the surrounding elements or components.

Another problem connected indirectly with movement in the ground is the transmission of transport movement, caused by heavy lorries or trains. Buildings adjacent to roads taking vehicle traffic of up to 40 tonnes can suffer from vibrations travelling through the ground to the foundations and lower parts of the structure. These vibrations flow through the structural materials, and in the worst cases can cause a building to shudder. Buildings over or adjacent to busy train lines (and especially underground systems or tunnels) will also suffer from vibrations.

The Convention Centre at the National Exhibition Centre in Birmingham straddles the rail line from London to the north-west of England. This passes through a tunnel. In order to ensure that no noise from the trains enters the auditoria the foundations had to be specially designed. As the sound travels via vibrations through the ground the piles needed to be protected and prevented from carrying the sound into the main structure. This was not only to ensure quietness, but also to leave the building free from the physical effects of noise and movement vibrations. In order to do this the piles were taken well below the level of the railway line and in addition those piles in close proximity to the tunnel were isolated from the ground at the junction between the top of the pile and cap and the sub-ground element of the building. The pile and cap were enveloped in a casing in contact with the ground, leaving the top of the pile in air, and therefore not in physical contact with the surrounding sub-soil. As a gap was left between the two solid masses (pile and ground) any vibrations emanating from the trains via the ground cannot be transferred to the top of the piles. An absorbent compound was placed between the top of the pile and the underside of the pile cap to further reduce the possibility of vibration transfer.

Wear and tear

Wear and tear mainly occurs *within* a building as it is a by-product of the use of the building by people. It can affect the decorations, surface finishes (such as floor coverings), doors and their furniture, and mechanical appliances such as lifts and plumbing installations. Wear and tear is most likely to occur at openings in the external envelope such as doors and windows. This phenomenon must be seen as a naturally occurring event and, therefore, all involved in design and construction must bear it in mind. For example, the floor coverings used in an access corridor would need to be of a heavier specification than those used in an area where the user activity is primarily sedentary. The level of use of a particular building area or component should dictate the specification. Generally, the heavier the use, the better the quality (and robustness) of components and finishings required. Unfortunately, many design decisions are based on initial cost criteria and not on expected use. This leads to inferior, unsuitable or, in some cases, unsafe components being fitted. Sooner rather than later these components will need repair or even replacement.

Public building owners or lessees can be held liable for failing to maintain a building's fabric and utilities to a standard which does not lead to accidents by users. Buildings such as shops should have surfaces suffering from wear and tear repaired without delay, to ensure that customers have safe access and egress.

Vandalism

Increasingly, buildings in urban industrial and city centre environments are subject to vandalism. This can range from bill posting and spray-painted graffiti to physical damage and arson. In some instances these acts are carried out by those living in the buildings, such as on housing estates.

Some commentators believe that there is a connection between design and vandalism, generalisations being frequently made that an environment with bare, cold concrete surfaces is more susceptible to graffiti, that functional but bare entrance halls are more prone to damage, and that long, artificially lit access corridors to flats suffer greater damage than short, naturally lit passages. The orientation of windows and doors over common areas can influence the incidence of vandalism. Those areas overlooked at ground level by occupiers are less prone to physical damage. It would appear vandals are less likely to be active when they are in view of others. Others suggest that vandalism is a social problem resulting from a lack of discipline in the school and/or home, combined with idle time resulting from unemployment. It is certain, however, that careful environmental design can help reduce the level of vandalism.

Vandals may smash glass, break doors, pull off door furniture, spray paint surfaces, break lights and foul walls, pavements and corridors. If such actions are repeated after repair then the process of general fabric deterioration is accelerated.

Accident

Although uncommon, accidents can cause building deterioration. A fire, even if contained and quickly extinguished, can affect adjacent areas. Damage is caused not only by the fire itself but also by the water needed to put it out. This may seep into concealed areas of the building and cause unseen deterioration. A fire may also weaken a building's structure, eventually leading to premature structural failure.

Other forms of accidental damage include impact from vehicles or projected objects. Buildings close to roads can be hit by vehicles themselves in an accident. Buildings such as factories and warehouses with vehicles operating inside them are particularly susceptible to accidental damage. Damage and deterioration can also be caused by chemical spillage, water taps being left on, blocked drains, etc.

Pest attack

Pest attack is a minor occurrence, perhaps, but one that can have a major effect on a building, according to the type of pest and the severity of the attack. Timber is vulnerable to woodworm and beetle attack in most countries of the world. In Africa, termites and ants can quickly devastate a wooden structure. In the UK, certain areas of the country are plagued with timber-boring beetles. Brickwork is attacked by wasps and birds.

Rodents can cause problems by gnawing through cables or blocking underfloor ventilation with their nests. There are also health risks to the occupants due to droppings left in habitable areas, particularly where food is stored or prepared.

INTERRELATIONSHIP OF AGENCIES OF DETERIORATION

Deterioration of a building occurs within a matrix of the agencies set out in Fig. 2.1. In any one building the influence of each will vary, but it can be argued that the main agency is the form of construction. In the past this would not have been held true, as knowledge about the behaviour of materials and components *in situ* and acting together had not been analysed. Today, there is a wealth of information and data on the performance of most common materials and components. The life of softwood timber can be ascertained, and the behaviour of all types of bricks predicted under prevailing weather conditions. The strength and durability of concrete is known, and the performance of metals in building has been well researched. The designer and builder have easy access to detailed and exhaustive research data. There is a constant stream of papers produced on the performance of materials. The building technologist should consult this data bank before designing and/or constructing. Nowadays, there can be little excuse for a material or component to fail in the short term due to climate, wear and tear or pollution. Ground movement may be more unpredictable, but if an adequate site investigation has been carried out then any problems should be identifiable. It is the responsibility of the technologist to satisfy himself that the ground is suitable for the purpose in the long term.

There is a particular connection between wear and tear and the incidence of vandalism. Where buildings are neglected and the worn-out parts are not repaired there is a tendency to be less careful on the part of the building's users. An attitude based on the idea 'if the owners don't care about the building, why should we?' can easily be generated. This can lead to accelerated internal decay. A building of poor external appearance may be a prime target for vandals and it signifies a lack of respect for the built environment. It may be that the building is not maintained adequately for valid reasons, such as planning blight. This could be due to a planned future demolition for road widening or general clearance. Obviously, money will not be spent on a building which has a short life. Unfortunately, this neglect could considerably shorten the life of the building and make it untenable for the users. Early evacuation may then be necessary and the building will stand as an eyesore for a number of years prior to demolition. During this time further vandalism is likely and the structure may become dangerous. The owners are liable and will either need to take remedial action or demolish the building at their own cost.

Although neglect leading to evacuation may not be too important as far as the continuation of the building is concerned, its presence in that state can have psychological effects on the surrounding community. One of the major reasons given for inner city unrest and riots is the state of the environment. Lord Scarman, in his report in the wake of the Brixton riots in 1983, cited the living conditions of the residents as a contributory factor in social unrest. Many lived in poor quality housing, whether modern (built mainly in the 1950s and '60s) or older (dating to the turn of the twentieth century). This housing had not been adequately maintained, irrespective of ownership, leading to a general attitude of apathy and disrespect. Of course, there can be no excuse for public disorder and riots, with their consequent damage to property and injury to people, but there is a link between the quality of housing provision, the general care of the surrounding environment, and levels of vandalism and violence. The improvement of the built environment cannot be carried out in isolation from improvements in the social fabric of the local society. Measures giving residents greater control over their own environment should be encouraged, especially in the case of those living on estates and in dwellings in public ownership. The owner-occupier has a direct vested interest in the upkeep of his property and the public sector tenant has none: all control is usually in the hands of the local authority, which controls rents, the allocation of tenancies and all maintenance and repair. Perhaps by giving local groups of tenants greater control over their particular blocks of flats or estates the general level of care for buildings might improve. The current (1988) government's policy of encouraging home ownership by allowing council tenants to purchase their occupied dwellings is intended, amongst other objectives, to allow pride of possession to manifest itself in the maintenance of the property. If this pride is projected to all buildings by most people in society, extremes of vandalism, and rates of deterioration, could be drastically reduced.

The opening remarks of this discussion focused on construction form as the main determinant of rates of deterioration. These rates are dependant upon climate, of course, and it is possible that damage can be caused which is not entirely foreseen. Examples include strong gusting winds taking off roofs, and gales flooding a building. Repairs and drying-out procedures may remedy immediate damage but in the long term irreparable deterioration can lead to buildings becoming uninhabitable.

This occurred in the 1970s in Florence, when the Italian city suffered major floods. Many of the affected buildings have now been vacated as they remain damp: decorations and wall finishes fall off and health is affected by the moist atmosphere. Leaving these buildings unoccupied also accelerates the rate of deterioration.

Another unforeseen factor could be excessive pollution coupled with extreme weather conditions causing severe damage, for example, if strong winds and storms bring acid rain.

Most buildings suffer deterioration from a combination of all or some of the listed agencies. At different parts of the year, according to the season, and through various stages of the building's life, they may be subject to one more than another. For example, a building experiencing heavy use – say, a factory gearing production over 24 hours, seven days a week, to meet short-term production targets – would suffer from unusual wear and tear. Particularly harsh cold winters could take their toll on all buildings in that locality. A plague of rodents could bring problems. A long, dry summer, as occurred in the UK in 1976, could cause excessive drying of clay soils leading to the settlement of buildings. (In 1976, claims of insurance compensation to repair unsound buildings were one hundred times greater in the UK than in the previous year.)

Periods of increased social unrest and/or unemployment, coupled with inadequate funds for repair and maintenance, can dramatically increase the deterioration of buildings. Accident is seen as a relatively minor and obviously unpredictable factor, but if the design and workmanship of a building were not up to standard in the first place then the likelihood of deterioration following an accident increases. Effective maintenance and repair to the required standards can prevent or at least slow down any further deterioration.

This introductory chapter has listed the main agencies of deterioration and briefly shown where they interrelate and how they contribute to the overall deterioration of a building. All these agencies can determine the life of the building or an individual material or component, but it must be appreciated that many materials do have a limited life, and that age takes its toll. This latter point is discussed by Cowell in *Ageing – an aspect of long-term maintenance* (CIOB Maintenance Information Service, 1978).

The next chapter will present a further discussion on ageing, with respect to materials and their properties, in relation to maintenance needs. Chapter 6 will look closely at the relationship between design and construction with particular reference to the occurrence of defects arising from poor detailing or procedures. Chapter 7 will describe investigation procedures to determine maintenance needs, and the repair of defects.

QUESTIONS

1. Consider the building you are now in and describe which agencies of deterioration are taking precedence.
2. Discuss which aspects of the local climate have the greatest effect on a building.
3. 'A building should be designed and built to last forever.' Discuss.

5. Materials

This chapter will illustrate how the properties of some materials aid and abet the process of deterioration. As an understanding develops of the relationship between a material's characteristics and the deterioration process, strategies for preventing and delaying decay can be specified and implemented.

TIMBER

There are two main classes of woods: *hardwoods* and *softwoods*. The chemical components of timber fibres are cellulose and hemicellulose, bonded together by lignin. Softwood generally contains more lignin than hardwood. The average proportions of the three major constituents in dry wood are: 45% to 60% cellulose, 10% to 25% hemicellulose and 20% to 35% lignin. There are other minor constituents which result in characteristic features in certain species. Most woods are slightly acidic and will produce acetic acid in damp conditions. Tannins in wood, in contact with iron or compounds of iron in the presence of moisture, will cause dark stains. Silica in hardwoods will blunt cutting tools, and gums and resins adversely affect working properties and the ability to take glue and surface finishes. Oily timbers such as teak may need to be de-greased before gluing or before applying surface finishes.

The density of timber varies widely between species, but most fall within the range 385–835kg/m^3. Within a range of moisture contents of 5% to 25%, the weight of timber varies by approximately 0.5% for every 1% variation in moisture content. As timber dries from its green condition the cell walls begin to dry. This process can be reversed by re-wetting the timber. Timber which has been seasoned will respond to variations in atmospheric humidity.

Timber is a good insulator. Its conductivity (k) is 0.144W/m deg C and transmittance (U) for 102mm thickness is approximately 1.2W/m^2 deg C for timber weighing 481kg/m^3 with 20% moisture content. Timber weighing 561kg/m^3 and having 12% moisture content will also have the same U value. In the latter case an increase in moisture content will worsen the U value.

The coefficient for thermal movement is 30–60 $\times$ 10^{-6} across the fibres and about one-tenth as much parallel to the fibres. Expansion joints are not normally required, even in large structures.

Timber must be considered as a combustible material, yet, depending on its thickness, it can offer some fire resistance. Timber is ignited at about 220–300°C, and being organic it will produce highly toxic carbon monoxide and large quantities of smoke. Softwoods and hardwoods typically char at a rate of about 0.6mm and 0.4mm per minute respectively. As burning proceeds the charcoal insulates the interior and there is little loss of strength with a large rise in temperature, and no increase in length. Additionally, its good thermal insulation properties will prevent a marked rise in the temperature of members on the side remote from the fire. The known spread of charring, dimensional stability and retention of strength by timber in fires allows its performance to be predicted.

Softwoods show good chemical resistance, resulting from a high cellulose and lignin content, coupled with a low hemicellulose content, low permeability, straight grain and small moisture movement. Wood has a relatively good resistance to alkalis and weak acids. The probability of inorganic salts from soils or damp masonry causing decomposition is minor.

Timber has a high strength to weight ratio, both in tension and compression, and is elastic. Structural timber has to meet minimum density requirements, and generally its strength increases with density. Its strength is reduced as moisture content rises, however. Timber with 28–30% moisture (*the fibre saturation point*) is only two-thirds the strength if at 12% moisture content. A 1°C temperature rise also reduces strength, by about 0.3%. A system of grading timber according to stress-resistance is practised in the UK. This is normally undertaken by machine but can be visual. It enables the strength properties of timber to be assessed so individual pieces can be reliably used as engineering members (see BS 4878: 1973 for a description of the system).

Causes of deterioration in timber

The main causes of deterioration in timber are: (a) mechanical effects, such as caused by excessive loads, abrasion or erosion; (b) sunlight, causing embroilment of the surface; (c) chemicals, as already mentioned; (d) bacteria, giving surface discoloration; (e) fungi, in both wet and moist conditions; and (f) marine borers and insects.

The durability of timber is synonymous with its resistance to fungal attack. Non-destructive fungi such as moulds do not damage timber but form a powder coating. Staining fungi feed mainly on starch and sugar in sapwood cells so that timber is not appreciably weakened. Affected woods take up moisture more readily, and paint can be pushed off.

The destructive fungi (or 'rots') cause the greatest problems. Dry rot (*merulium lacrymans* in the UK) usually spreads more extensively, causes more damage and is more difficult to eradicate than wet rot. The timber is colonised by minute hyphae which can spread over surfaces and through minute cracks in brickwork, plaster and other materials. Strands can enable the hyphae to colonise adjacent timber. Dry rot is generally found indoors, in timber which has been slowly moistened, often by contact with damp brickwork, in stable conditions. The maximum temperature allowing growth is 26°C, the optimum 23°C, and below 3°C the rot remains inactive. The optimum moisture content of the wood is 30% to 40%. Wet rot in the UK is commonly in the form of *coniophora cerebella*, a white or 'soft' rot.

The prevention of deterioration

From the foregoing it can be seen that timber is a cellular material, able to absorb water; it is combustible, and liable, in the right conditions, to fungal, beetle and insect attack. In order to prevent deterioration, some form of treatment needs to be applied, and for this chemical preservatives are used. These penetrate into the timber cells and give protection from fungal and insect attacks over a long period of time. Suitable methods of applying wood preservatives are given in BRE Digest 201, *Wood preservatives: application methods*. In essence, the greater the depth of penetration into the core of the timber member, the more effective the preservative.

Paint can give some protection to timber from the effects of the weather. It will prevent the absorption of rain water into the wood, resist the drying effect of the sun and give the wood a pleasing appearance. Paint is only a surface coating and will penetrate to just below the surface. Therefore, it can peel off quite easily if not applied properly. Alternatively, coloured preservatives which will penetrate deeper into the wood can be used. The range of colours is limited in comparison to paint, and finishes such as gloss are not easily obtainable. They are claimed to last longer than paint before the need to recoat.

The absorption property of timber is both its weakness and its strength. Its weakness in that it can readily take in water which can lead to fungal attack and loss of strength, but its strength is that preservatives can penetrate to its core to provide the required protection.

BRICKS

The following discussion of bricks will be confined to those manufactured from clay as classified in BS 3921: Part 2: 1969, *Bricks and blocks of fired earth, clay or shale*.

The appearance of bricks varies according to type of clay, type of superficial colouring applied to facing bricks, and texture of finish. A wide range of colours and textures is now available.

Clay bricks can have compressive strengths of up to $180N/mm^2$, although Class A engineering bricks are $6.9N/mm^2$. The highest load-bearing brick in normal use is around $103N/mm^2$. Lower strengths than this are quite suitable for low-rise structures. Strength is not necessarily an index of durability. Those in the upper classes are usually durable but there are bricks approaching this strength which decay rapidly if exposed to freezing temperatures in wet conditions, and others, much weaker, which are more durable.

As bricks are porous they will absorb water. The rate of absorption is expressed as a percentage of the dry weight of a brick. It can vary from less than 3% to about 30%. Water absorption figures do not necessarily indicate the behaviour of a brick in weathering, however. A low absorption rate, of less than 7% by weight, usually indicates a high resistance to damage by freezing, although some bricks capable of much higher absorption may also be frost resistant. There is no simple correlation between absorption and resistance. Some types of bricks with an absorption of 8–12% by weight will cover the range from resistant to non-resistant to frost damage. Another type of brick with a range of absorption from 12% to 18% might still be frost resistant, even at its highest absorption rate.

Under BS 3921 there is no requirement for a frost test, but bricks are deemed to be frost resistant if they satisfy one of the following requirements:

(a) The manufacturer shall provide evidence that the bricks have given satisfactory service in conditions at least as severe as those proposed for not less than three years in the locality for which their use is being considered.

(b) In the absence of such evidence, a sample panel should be built in the locality in an exposed position which is independently assessed. This to remain in place for three years and if the bricks have performed well they are deemed to be suitable.

(c) When neither of the above is possible an engineering brick classed by strength and/or water absorption shall be deemed to be frost resistant.

Causes of deterioration in brick and their prevention

In the UK, frost damage is relatively rare in external walls between DPCs and eaves, but it is not uncommon in retaining walls, free-standing walls and parapets, especially if bricks have not been selected carefully. Any frost damage to walls between eaves and DPC is usually in areas of severe exposure.

All bricks contain some soluble salts, which may also be present in the mortar. They can produce efflorescence or staining. If bricks becomes saturated in stack prior to being laid the probability of the salts appearing as a white or near white deposit is increased. A test described in BS 3921 can be undertaken to assess the probable behaviour of a brick with regard to its propensity for efflorescence. Common locations for efflorescence are parapets and earth-retaining walls, and where deficiencies in design may allow excessive water to get into the brickwork. In such cases staining may occur on the mortar in the joints. If this risk is known it is advisable to postpone pointing and allow the stain to materialise on the raked out joint, and then point over it.

All ordinary Portland cements contain tricalcium aluminate which can react with sulphates in solution. This can cause the brickwork to expand owing to the expansion of the mortar joints. Progressive deterioration of the mortar joints can follow. Movement is greater vertically than horizontally. Repeated wetting and drying of parapets and free-standing walls is most likely to result in deterioration.

The coefficient of linear thermal expansion of clay bricks is taken as 5×10^{-6} per °C. The behaviour of walls is difficult to predict owing to the restraint due to internal friction or internal restriction. As the internal and external surfaces of a wall can be heated unequally there may be a tendency to differential movement within the wall thickness. Any reversal of this movement will in all probability be restricted by friction and other effects.

On cooling after firing in the kiln, bricks start to take up moisture from the air and initially expand at a high rate. This movement may continue at a slow and diminishing rate indefinitely. Tests at the Building Research Establishment have shown that a brick can expand by about 0.8mm per metre in the first eight years, of which half the expansion occurs in the first week. A moderately fired engineeering brick can have a larger expansion of up to 1.6mm per metre. Knowledge of the behaviour of bricks and brick walls is still being gathered, but evidence suggests that the ratio of brickwork expansion to brick expansion is 0.6 if no other expansion agencies, such as sulphates in mortar, are present. There is also a small, reversible wetting-and-drying movement of up to 0.02% which does not appear to lessen in time.

Clay bricks provide excellent fire resistance and CP 121: Part I:

1973 gives minimum thicknesses of plastered and unplastered walls for the various standards of resistance.

Generally, the ageing of bricks and brickwork enhances their appearance and does not materially affect decay, although some older, softer bricks are affected by spalling due to freezing and thawing of rain and sleet in the pores. Polluted atmospheres can change the appearance of bricks by making them darker. The greater deterioration occurs on the mortar joints. These may require repointing after the old mortar has been raked out to a depth of at least 20mm. Lichens, moulds and similar growths can occur on areas away from direct sunlight taking heavy falls of rain.

Bricks require no further treatment to prolong their life, except in the situations mentioned where they may need to be replaced due to excessive spalling. There are a number of other factors which can cause damage and deterioration due to the inherent properties of brick, namely thermal movement and the use of unsound materials in the manufacture of the brick, such as unslaked lime nodules. BRE Digests 200, *Repairing brickwork*, and 89, *Sulphate attack on brickwork*, describe the common problems and suggest methods of repair and maintenance. BRE Digest 160, *Mortars for bricklaying*, gives a comprehensive review of the types, selection and mixing of mortars for brickwork.

CONCRETE

There is a wealth of information available on all aspects of concrete specification, design and quality control, its problems and its use with reinforcement. It is not appropriate here, however, to consider the matter in too much detail. Only general aspects will be considered in order to illustrate the connection between the properties of the material and deterioration. What is significant is that even with the current state of knowledge in concrete technology there is still much to be learnt. For example, the problem of carbonation is now only just being understood, yet buildings exhibiting symptoms of this form of decay were built in the later 1960s and early 1970s.

The properties of concrete are essentially as follows. It is considerably stronger under compression than in tension. It is subject to 'creep', depending largely on the aggregate used, illustrating plastic deformation under constant load; this occurs rapidly at first but slowly approaches a limit after about five years. The degree of creep is roughly in proportion to the load applied, and is greater with weaker and less mature concretes. A good, compacted concrete with a low water/cement ratio has good resistance to the absorption of water. No concrete is completely impervious to water vapour and admixtures can sometimes contribute to impermeability. The chemical resistance of ordinary Portland cement concrete increases with crushing strength (BRE Current Paper 23/77, *Chemical resistance of concrete*, gives further details).

Causes of deterioration in concrete and their prevention

Frost can attack concrete in capillary pores or cracks through the expansion of ice crystals. These pores or cracks may be formed by the evaporation of excess water used in the mix. Discontinuous pores which improve resistance to frost can be created by air-entrainment admixtures, which can enhance concrete's overall durability.

In temperatures above 102°C concrete suffers a serious loss of strength, with flexural strength being more affected than compressive strength. Its performance in fire depends upon the presence of reinforcement and the type of aggregate. In reinforced concrete there is little residual strength above 600°C. The average value of the coefficient of thermal expansion is approximately 10×10^{-6} deg C. This means that with a 40°C rise in temperature a 30m long beam will expand by about 12mm.

When concrete dries it shrinks, and in its initial curing stages this shrinkage is irreversible. This is assumed not to exceed 0.045% and requires no special attention at the design stage. Certain aggregates do exhibit high volume changes on wetting and drying, which may lead to concretes made with them having drying shrinkages four times those obtained with non-shrinkable aggregates. This problem is fully discussed in BRE Digest 35, *Shrinkage of natural aggregates in concrete*.

Concrete is prone to attack by sulphate-bearing soils or where in contact with ground waters carrying sulphates. Some colliery shale used as underfloor fill has naturally occurring sulphates and this can attack overlying concrete floors, causing expansion and cracking.

CONCLUSION

The three common construction materials – timber, brick and concrete – demonstrate a direct link between their properties and their propensity to deteriorate. In order to prolong their life and protect them from damage some form of maintenance needs to be carried out. This must be based on a scientific understanding of the material and its performance in use. This latter aspect can cause problems. While there is much scientific knowledge relating to individual materials, there is little relating to their performance in use, especially when they are combined to form components or elements. There are two factors to be considered here: the initial compatibility of materials, and their compatibility under the conditions of use. For example, brick and concrete are compatible. Placing them together does not create reactions or deterioration. Placed in an exposed position, however, performing under loads, one or both may fail quickly. Timber in ideal conditions will last indefinitely, indeed in the UK there are examples of exposed hardwood timber-framed buildings dating back to the fourteenth century. But untreated softwood adjacent to damp brickwork can disintegrate within a period of ten years. This occurred in some timber framed bungalows built in Cornwall relatively recently. Weather penetration, rising damp and interstitial condensation all contributed to wet rot, which was only discovered when the frame of one bungalow was uncovered for an extension to be added. Virtually all strength was lost from the timber frame and the bungalows needed to be completely rebuilt. Guarantees and insurance cover do not prevent or solve the problem of failure. It is the knowledge of the building technologist which should be exercised in designing and building elements and buildings which require minimal maintenance, let alone complete rebuilding. A sound analytical understanding of a material's characteristics and performance must be an essential ingredient of construction knowledge.

The main points to be taken from this chapter are that there is a direct connection between the properties of the material and the effect that the agencies of deterioration have *because* of those properties. Therefore, there is a need to ensure that effective measures are adopted to maintain the integrity of the material and/or the component/element with which the material is associated. Deterioration may also be affected by the proximity of other materials, and the position of the material with respect to the building's form and local climatic conditions. These general principles are related to timber in Fig. 2.2. The cellular structure of timber gives it strength, but also allows the easy absorption of water, which needs to be prevented by some form of treatment. Owing to its constituent chemical and organic make-up it can provide a habitat for beetles or food for termites. Again, preservatives can prevent attack, as can location. The proximity of other materials can affect the integrity of timber and its compatibility to them, and the environment should always be analysed. It seems absurd that the majority of timber window frames fitted to new houses in the UK over the last twenty years have been made from softwood, when the climatic conditions are generally wet, cool and not suited to small softwood sections. The quality of the imported softwood has not been of the highest standards (it does not need to meet any structural criteria) and this, coupled with

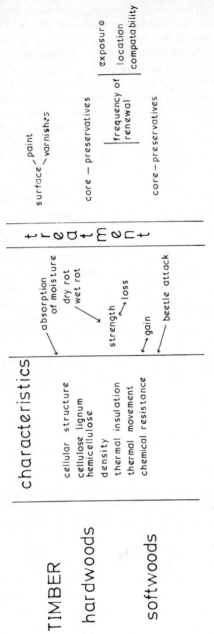

Fig. 2.2 *The relation between material properties and*
deterioration

poor specifications for surface coatings, has led to large numbers of premature failures, mainly because the softwood has become saturated with rainwater. Subsequently, repainting has blistered, flaked or rolled off owing to dampness in the wood, and this dampness has led to loss of strength and the splitting of the timber. Although these problems can be found in much older buildings, these have lasted up to a hundred years before failing, mainly due to the larger cross-sectional areas used in window members, the better quality of the softwood used, and a higher initial specification for the surface coating. If poorer quality softwoods are employed, therefore, they will require a higher standard of protection and maintenance to sustain their appearance and integrity.

The next chapter tackles the question of quality in terms of design and construction criteria and making the best of materials. These will be considered in the context of the interrelationship between the functions and roles of designer and builder. The problem of correlating the scientific knowledge of material characteristics and performance with the correct formulation of materials and components into elements will be addressed in Part Four of this volume.

QUESTIONS

1. Consider the essential properties of plastics and describe how they have been adapted for use in buildings, and the measures adopted to prevent their decay. (See BRE Digests 69, *Durability and application of plastics*; 224, *Cellular plastics for building*; and 161, *Reinforced plastic cladding panels*.)
2. Using an example of one of the common construction metals, such as steel, aluminium or copper, show the range of influence the agencies of deterioration have upon it.
3. 'An understanding of the processes of material deterioration is essential before determining maintenance strategies.' Discuss.

6. Construction Form

DETERIORATION IN HOUSING

As has already been pointed out, the greatest agency of deterioration affecting materials and components is their original design and subsequent construction processes and techniques. An important publication based on research by the Building Research Establishment – *Quality in traditional housing*, HMSO, 1982: Volume 1: *An investigation into faults and their avoidance*; Volume 2: *An aid to design*; Volume 3: *An aid to site inspection* – has shown that defects in design and construction can lead to an increase in the rate of deterioration. Approximately 55% of the faults noted could be attributed to poor or inadequate design, and the remaining 45% to construction operations. The report found that a considerable number of the traditional houses inspected had a fault which would cause a significant problem if not rectified.

What is particularly disturbing about the overall findings of the BRE report is that it is based on low-rise, traditional housing, i.e. on structures based on load-bearing brick walls standing on standard concrete foundations, with solid concrete ground floors, timber upper floors and trussed rafter roofs. Apart from trussed rafter roofs this form of construction has been practised in the UK since the mid-nineteenth century, with, of course, some improvements in foundation and wall design, and in construction. After a period of nearly 150 years this well-known, basic form of construction can no longer satisfy performance requirements. Although it can be seen that some performance requirements have increased since the turn of the twentieth century, the fundamental requirements of durability, weather-tightness, strength and stability have remained constant. Similarly, the overall climate of the UK is little changed. On the other hand, knowledge of materials and their performance has increased dramatically, to the benefit, it would be hoped, of design and construction. Information of this kind is readily available both from independent sources such as the Building Research Establishment and from material suppliers and product manufacturers.

Common faults in traditional housing

In theory, the long years of practical experience, coupled with the increase in scientific knowledge, should ensure that ordinary houses are built without avoidable faults. Unfortunately, this is not the case. Before discussing the reasons for this, a few of the problems will be described, together with their contribution to the reduction in integrity of the building. Confining the problem to the stages of construction between wall construction and the fitting of first-floor joists, the list is as follows.

The notation in brackets refers to the source of advice or the requirement relating to a particular item: BR refers to Building Regulations; CP (with number) to the relevant Code of Practice; BRE (with number) to the relevant BRE Digest; Agrément Board of Certification recommendation.

1. Damp-proof course pointed over or bridged by driveways and paths. (BR)
2. Quality of bricks and blockwork used in external walls: inadequate thermal insulation; displaced and damaged bricks and blocks; unfilled joints. (CP 121)
3. Inadequate window and door sections: arris not sanded; stops not fixed; timber not treated with preservative.
4. Wall ties, quality and insulation: number of wall ties or degree of protection inadequate; wall ties sloping the wrong way; drip not in centre of cavity; contamination by mortar droppings. (BR; CP 121)
5. Bricks in inner leaf reducing insulation. (BR)
6. Defective weather-proofing at end of separating wall. (BR)
7. Buttressing walls: minimum return length not observed; maximum size of opening exceeded. (BR)
8. Damp-proof course less than 150mm above ground level. (BR)
9. Flimsy window opening lights.
10. Joints between window head and external wall: too large; unfilled. (BR)
11. Lintels in external walls: absent; damaged bedding; damaged insulation. (CP 121)
12. Support to blockwork partitions from below: inappropriate; inadequate. (CP 121)
13. Noggings, blockings and struttings: missing or ineffective in floors. (CP 112)
14. Back-to-back chasing for services. (BR. BRE 252)
15. Holes in blockwork at joist ends.
16. No conduits or sleeves provided for services passing through walls. (BR)
17. Joist hangers in floors: damaged; not tightly fitting. (Agrément)

18. Trimmers poorly supported.
19. Lintels in internal walls: broken; bearings ineffective. (CP 121)
20. Cavity trays not provided. (CP 121)
21. No lateral restraint to separating walls. (BR)
22. Gaps or unfilled joints in separating walls. (BR; BRE 252)
23. Floor joists, quality and installation: not graded or marked; bowed and twisted; high moisture content; wet rot. (CP 112; BRE 252)
24. Blocks not achieving satisfactory values for sound insulation. (BR; BRE 252)
25. Inappropriate or defective sub-sills in external walls: no damp-proof course; tiles not laid to break joint. (CP 121; BRE 77)
26. Meter boxes: damaged; no cavity tray or lintel.
27. Reveals in external walls damaged, so vulnerable to water penetration. (CP 121)

The above list is not exhaustive, and includes only about 20% of the total number of problems found. As can be judged, some faults cannot be put down to ignorance. For example, all building personnel should know that the damp-proof course should be a minimum of 150mm above the adjoining finished ground level. Some faults can be directly attributed to the designer, where they involve the sizes of openings or flimsy window opening lights. Other faults are the responsibility of the builder, as with the bridging of wall cavities and the poor support of trimmers.

In their effect on the integrity of the house structure and envelope the faults can be translated into the following categories:

Maintenance and durability	40%
Strength and stability	20%
Ventilation, heating and condensation	8%
Weather-tightness and rising damp	5%
Thermal insulation	5%
Sound	4%
Fire	4%
Other	14%

Maintenance and durability are most affected by faults, putting the long-term health of a building at risk. Durability will be shortened, and although it is possible that this can be prevented, it will take time, energy and money to rectify.

Some faults do not immediately manifest themselves. An example of this is the inadequate bedding of an external lintel. As time progresses the lintel may settle differentially, or weather may penetrate and affect the integrity of the lintel itself, by corroding the metal. Rain may seep under the lintel by capillary attraction

into the causes of defects, their overall incidence and the apportionment of liability between architect and builder.

CONCLUSION

To summarise, this chapter has put forward the view that many problems of building deterioration are caused by those engaged in the processes of design and construction. Information and data about the performance of materials are easily available, but are frequently ignored. This situation can be improved by enhancing standards of knowledge and by introducing more extensive educational and training courses, both prior to qualification and after qualification, allowing continuing professional development.

QUESTIONS

1. Describe a site procedure that could be implemented to ensure that timber products are prevented from early deterioration.
2. Discuss the responsibility of the designer in preventing undue deterioration of the fabric.
3. Discuss the feasibility of introducing quality assurance procedures on a construction site.

7. Investigation Procedures

Procedures for appraising or investigating buildings are determined by the purpose of the investigation. Is it to give a value for the building? Is it to assess its feasibility with regard to conversion? Is it to investigate a particular visible problem? Or is it simply to record what is there? In this chapter the main techniques of investigation will be described. A closer analysis will be made of the techniques associated with investigating problems and defects, and, finally, a few examples will illustrate particular procedures with respect to components and materials.

Figure 2.3 shows the main types of investigation procedures, which are described below.

TECHNIQUES OF INVESTIGATION

Record

It may be necessary to record a building exactly. This can be done by accurately measuring the building, or parts thereof, and preparing scale-dimensioned drawings. These drawings can be supplemented with sketches or photographs. The photographs can aid the accurate drawing-up of the site visit notes, or form a permanent record together with the drawings. A complete discussion of methods of taking on-site dimensions and recording them is given in Staveley, H.S., *Measured dimensional surveys*, CIOB Technical Information Service, 1984. Descriptive text or full annotations on the drawings could provide further explanations where detail is difficult to show. This type of survey is carried out prior to the submission of any new proposals for a building. It may also be done prior to demolition as an historic record. Plans and elevations of buildings are required for gaining statutory approvals under planning and building regulations.

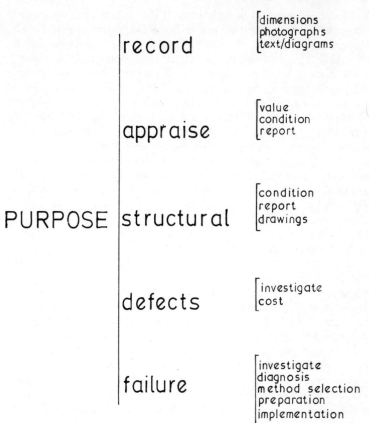

Fig. 2.3   *Investigation procedures*

Appraisal

A general impression of the shape, form, use and condition of an estate or a group of buildings is often required. The National Health Service in the UK has developed a computer-based program into which data is fed which can give a return of information regarding the general characteristics of buildings. This is described in Smith, R.N.B., *Condition appraisals and their use*, CIOB Technical Information Service, 1985. The type of information stored on the first program includes: site summary; tenure; relevant authorities and utilities; rights over land; restrictions and easements; sub-soil information; town planning information; statistics; block summary; block detail (e.g. date built, heated volume, aggregate condition); and legal requirements.

A second program records an analysis of the physical condition of the estate or group of buildings. It is divided into 19 elements and each is given a standard of condition ranging from A to D. The elements are: structure; external fabric; roof; internal fabric; internal fixtures and fittings; external works and grounds; electrical installation; heating system; steam system; ventilation; phones and paging; alarms and safety systems; drainage; piped medical gas and vacuum; hot and cold water systems; lifts; boilers/ calorifier plant; fixed plant and equipment; fuel/storage and distribution. Condition A is the highest standard and is considered as new, whereas condition D is a category covering those elements in which there is a serious risk of imminent breakdown or where they are unacceptable on health and safety grounds. A form is provided to record the element and its condition, and an approximate cost on any upgrading necessary can also be logged. A condition appraisal file can be printed for each building, listing the elements, the condition category, the cost to repair, if applicable, the remaining life expectancy and the cost to upgrade. With minor adaptations this program could be used for any building or group of buildings. It provides an overall indication of the state of the buildings and can immediately highlight those elements which are causing problems, or may cause problems in the near future. Using this program effectively could initiate preventive maintenance.

Appraisals are also carried out to assess the value of a property, the most common example being a survey on a house with a view to obtaining a mortgage for its purchase. This appraisal considers the basic structure and condition of the building, but also considers it in relation to its surroundings. In arriving at a valuation of the property the current state of the market is also brought into the assessment. This may or may not be influenced by the local surroundings. For example, the area may be an inner-city block, with surrounding property of a low standard, with subsequent low values. The block in question, however, may have facilities and accommodation which are in high demand, and this will give it an enhanced value when compared to the surrounding properties. The actual condition of the property, within reason, may not drastically reduce its value if the building is thought to be in a desirable geographic position. In this case it might be the land which provides the enhanced value rather than the building. The prospects of the building with respect to the future development of the area will also affect its value. Are there going to be road improvements? Is the area changing, say from residential to commercial use, or vice versa?

Reports are prepared, usually on a descriptive basis, by valuers and/or estate agents, setting out the basic details of the property and giving an assessment of the value of the property.

Structural surveys

The primary purpose of a structural survey is to give an independent professional opinion on the structural condition of a property. In the UK the average general practitioner surveyor will not be capable of reporting on drainage, heating systems or electrical installations, and people carrying out surveys must have considerable experience in the performance of buildings and their components. The survey should be carried out systematically and each item recorded on paper or on tape. Working from a checklist the surveyor should examine the following: the site; outbuildings; drains; the building's exterior, including roof, floors, walls, windows and doors; electrical wiring; plumbing; space heating. Items which should receive extra scrutiny are, externally: chimney stacks; roof covering; gutters and rainwater pipes; main walls; windows; external doors; damp courses; sub-floor ventilation; insulation; levels; foundations. Internally: roof void; plastering; woodwork (for rot and beetle attack); windows and doors; floors; condensation. All drains, levels, manholes and septic tanks (disposal) should also be checked. The survey should be presented in the form of a written report in which the surveyor fully describes the property and its condition, together with any defects which exist or are likely to arise. A professional indemnity clause will also be inserted into the report stating, for example, that where inspection was not possible owing to inaccessibility the surveyor cannot be held liable for the effects of any problems. The surveyor should point out the good as well as the bad. Remedial measures for defects should be indicated if they are of immediate concern, and a priority list for future repairs, with some idea of present-day costs, may also be useful to the client.

The structural survey is a critical examination of all the aspects of a building with respect to their condition, present performance and future performance. A thoughtful, but in some instances, light-hearted, paper on structural surveys is published by the CIOB in its Maintenance Information Service series (Staveley, H.S., *Structural surveys*). It provides a general view of the purpose and nature of surveys, and the application of structural surveys to properties in the health service; it also gives a personal view on the practice of carrying out surveys.

Defect reports

Many problems in buildings arise with little or no warning, as with a broken window pane or a leak in a pipe. Such defects are quite obvious and are usually reported by the tenant or building user. Such information should be entered on a form stating the address, type of building, basic construction details and description of defect. Subsequently, the nature of the remedial action, together with its approximate cost, together with any other work involved, should also be entered on the form. It might be necessary to follow up the initial notification of the defect if its cause is unclear or unknown. A site visit can ascertain further details and may be the prelude to a thorough investigation. As visits to the building are costly these should only be carried out when doubt is expressed over the defect.

Organisations responsible for large numbers of properties – the Property Services Agency, the Health Service, Local Authorities, Housing Associations and commercial enterprises – should have a system of feedback of information on housing defects. This information should be recycled into two areas for consideration. First, the compilation of data on housing defects can lead to their prevention. For example, a historical record of a failure of a particular component could show that breakdown is likely after five years, before which time an inspection should be made, therefore. Second, the information on defects could be considered when designing new buildings or extensions to old buildings. Lessons learnt on the performance of components need to be incorporated into future constructions so as to reduce the probability of failure.

The Property Services Agency has developed a system of defect feedback which is justified by its need to reduce avoidable defects. Its essential characteristics are as follows:

1. It is a three-way process covering *feed-in* or the collection of information; *central recording*, storage, retrieval and analysis; and *feed-out* or dissemination.
2. It covers the life cycle of buildings, including the construction period.
3. It applies to all defects and failures in all buildings and civil engineering works excluding only trivial items and those due to fair wear and tear.
4. In the case of the PSA it is mandatory upon all those engaged throughout the UK on design, construction and maintenance.

The process of dissemination may not take place until after some time as laboratory tests and further investigation might be necessary via a Feedback Digest.

An example of the Feedback Digest is given in the CIOB Maintenance Information Service paper *Building defects and feedback in the PSA* (Randall, R.H., 1987). The example is based on the problem of water trapped below the waterproof layers of a flat roof. It describes the effects it might have on the roof, and the possible sources of the water, whether it is constructional water or rainwater. In connection with the latter the Digest presents charts, diagrams and statistics on rainfall for various locations in the UK, and analyses its effect on the flatroof construction. This is a prime example of matching the climatic conditions to the performance of buildings, and points to the care required during the construction process to prevent the entrapment of water. The flat roof construction itself is described with reference to the PSA's own specification clauses. The general rates of evaporation of standing water on the roof are discussed. The conclusion states:

There is a very good argument that, save in exceptional circumstances, all built-up flat roofing in the UK should be carried out under temporary protective coverings. Such protection is not cheap, but the alternative appears to be a continuation of expensive roof failures.

As far as the PSA is concerned these types of roofs should only be built or repaired under a protective covering. The information can reach those within the PSA, but information as vital as this deserves wider dissemination. All building owners, architects, specifiers and builders ought to be familiar with it. Many other areas of concern of equal importance remain unknown to a large number of people in the construction industry. The building defect reports published by the BRE should also be in common currency amongst all practitioners, together with those produced by client organisations.

Failure

In order to discover the reasons for a building failure a six-step approach should be followed:

1. *Investigation*. Search for the problem. The building element may need to be opened up, or have samples taken for further analysis or investigation in a laboratory. Monitoring over a period of time might be required. Full dimensional surveys and subsequent drawings, together with photographs, can form part of the investigation process. Testing devices such as the ultrasonic pulse velocity meter and moisture meters can be employed to give indications of the state of the materials.
2. *Diagnosis*. When all the available information has been collected together a diagnosis of the failure can be made. This diagnosis should consider all the particular aspects of the problem, and even though similar faults have been experienced the obvious conclusions should always be questioned. There is always an exception which breaks the rule. The diagnosis should fully detail the reasons for the failure, stating the evidence upon which the judgement is made.
3. *Plan operations*. What is the next stage? Is the fault one of many?: Or is it a one-off occurrence? How does it affect the

adjoining components and elements? What is its influence over the life of the building? The failure should be assessed in its overall relationship to the building, its user demands and who is to carry out the remedial work.

4. *Method selection.* The selection of the method of repair is dependent upon (a) the nature of the failure, (b) the environment (both at the site of the problem and around the whole building), (c) cost, and (d) desired final appearance.

5. *Preparation.* The area around the fault should be properly prepared. Temporary works should be in place, building users notified, and all plant, machinery and materials to hand. The repair should be prepared in accordance with the technological restraints pertaining to the materials and with regard to the safety of both the operatives and third parties.

6. *Implementation.* The repair work should be carried out to the last detail of the selected method. Any manufacturer's instructions should be followed, as should the rules of good practice expressed in published manuals and defect repair sheets. Adequate supervision of the work should be given.

A few examples, based on published research, can be described showing how the above principles can be put into practice. The first example is based on the investigation of wall cladding defects presented in BRE Digest No 217, *Wall cladding defects and their diagnosis.* A table of frequency of inspection is given below:

New buildings: older buildings after major repairs and alterations	Initially then annually for first five years
Parts of buildings where risk of damage by vehicle impact or vandals	Annually
Parts of buildings subject to severe exposure conditions, including all work above ninth floor of high structures	Every third year
Parts of all buildings over public areas	Every third year and after severe gales, heavy snowfall or other extremes of weather
Other buildings, and other parts of buildings in above categories	Every five years or when repainting is being scheduled if more frequent
Parts of buildings known to contain latent defects	As appropriate to the nature and seriousness of the defect

On cladding units or materials the problems to look for are

cracks, spalling, looseness and misalignment. Stains may not be serious but if accompanied by cracks may be an early indication that fixings or reinforcement are corroding.

The joints may show signs of ageing, such as the hardening and splitting of the sealant, or the amount and direction of relative movement. Where open-drained vertical joints are used, check that baffles are tucked under the flashing at the head and extend to the foot of the joint. Defects can be related to particular locations, such as between different cladding materials, between cladding and *in situ* work, at salient or re-entrant angles, and also at the locations most exposed to the weather, such as parapets. Incorrectly detailed work, as in the omission of throating under cills, can lead to problems.

Fixings are normally hidden and therefore their problems are not readily seen. Indications can be given by gaps between parts intended to be tightly connected, or by signs of distortion or displacement that might indicate overloading. Superficial corrosion may be an indication of massive future problems. Staining and disruptive expansion at points where fixings might be expected can indicate problems.

Design tolerances for fixing and construction inaccuracies are often inadequate, and poor modifications to surmount the problem may produce insecure fixings. Excessive gaps and improvised packing can show the result of problems.

Damp in a cavity can be due to rain penetration or condensation: if persistent this should be investigated, as damp conditions can lead to corrosion of fixings.

In brick, stone or precast concrete claddings, closure of joints, cracking and spalling can be symptoms of either vertical or horizontal compression. As the BRE Digest says, the correct diagnosis is not unlike the detection of crime, it is a matter of gathering evidence and testing it critically for compliance with known facts.

Latent defects are by their nature extremely difficult to ascertain. They are not normally visible until failure occurs and only by dismantling can they be discovered. A close inspection of the building's drawings, specifications and records of previous repairs may indicate possible problems. Buildings of similar type and construction can provide evidence of likely problems. For example, a fault in one type of system-built dwelling is quite likely to be found in other buildings of that genre, so dismantling investigation would be justified.

Defects should be accurately recorded. Even so-called trivial information can clarify the reasons for a failure. Sketches (with location and date marked) should be made of actual or potential defects and annotated with relevant dimensional information (for example, joint width and taper in elevation and the misalignment of faces on either side of a joint). Photographs (properly described and dated) can also lead to a greater understanding of the problems when studied together with other evidence off-site. The BRE Digest gives a comprehensive checklist of fault indications with their possible significance.

The problems of foundations and their investigation are described in BRE Digest No. 251, 1981, *Assessment of damage in low-rise buildings*. The Digest states that in the analysis of the incidence of foundation failures and the methods of their assessment and diagnosis, inadequate attention was paid to describing building damage. An essential first step in any assessment should be to ensure that all visible damage is properly recorded and classified in the terms of an objective, widely accepted scale. Descriptions are often too broad, while subjective assessments vary widely on the seriousness of problems. The Digest suggests the following procedure for carrying out a survey to assess the structural damage to houses caused, probably by some form of foundation failure:

1. On a sketch of each damaged wall, draw the position and direction of any cracks.
2. Try to determine the approximate age of the cracks.
3. Where possible, measure or estimate the magnitude of any distortion and movement of the building.
4. Describe how the serviceability of the building has been impaired.
5. Give a thorough description of the materials of walls and finishes and their condition, especially that of mortar.
6. Record details of the construction.
7. Where the cause of damage is believed to be foundation movement, additional factors may need to be considered, depending on the scale of damage sustained.

Each of the above operations is fully explained in the Digest. The above survey should make apparent the general cause of the damage. If this is due to progressive ground movement the following signs should be visible:

(a) Cracks usually show externally and internally, and may extend through the damp-proof course and down into the foundation.
(b) Crack tapers should be consistent with differential foundation movement. Crack patterns should be reasonably consistent with observed or measured distortions.
(c) Floors may slope, walls may tilt, and window and door openings may distort, producing uneven clearance and jamming.

In order to objectively assess the damage the Digest provides six categories on a scale 0 to 5:

0	negligible	crack up to 0.1mm
1	very slight	crack up to 1mm
2	slight	crack up to 5mm
3	moderate	crack 5 to 15mm
4	severe	crack 15 to 25mm
5	very severe	greater than 25mm, or depends on number

These categories can be directly entered onto drawings and other record documents. Similar categories, but with different values for crack width or gaps, are given for classifying the visible damage caused by floor slab movement.

Our final example is based on BRE Digest No. 257, 1982, *Installation of wall ties in existing construction*. The Digest describes the range of techniques currently available to insert wall ties into cavity walls that have either been damaged or have lost their connection between the leaves as a result of corrosion of steel wall ties. Some guidance is given on the process of appraisal to assess the extent of the problem and the need for repair. Installation of new wall ties into existing constructions may be needed (a) to reinstate masonry cavity walls damaged by expansive corrosion of vertical twist steel wall ties; (b) to reinstate cavity walls rendered unsafe or unstable through loss of wire ties by corrosion; (c) to increase the number of ties in walls built with insufficient ties connecting the leaves; (d) to tie back existing cladding walls to concrete, steel and timber frame structures; (e) to stabilise faced or collar jointed walls in cases where the outer layer is becoming detached from the backing; (f) to tie new walls or bulging walls back to existing cross walls; (g) to tie back walls on either side of cracks caused by subsidence or other damage; and (h) to tie back walls on either side of deliberate cuts made for insertion of openings or movement joints.

The best way to inspect existing ties is to remove bricks or other units from the outer leaf where the suspect ties are positioned. A fibre-optic device can be inserted for remote inspection, but the problem may be in the outer leaf bed joint where the corrosion cannot be seen. There are metal detectors which can detect metal ties, but these are not very accurate and need to be matched with either non-ferrous metals or stainless steels. The Digest lists a number of possible repair methods, comments on their suitability, advantages and disadvantages and also recommends the best tying system to solve a particular problem.

Laboratory testing

The three examples described above are directly related to site investigation, analysis with desk top information and then repair. With the increasing complexity of faults and their reasons it may be necessary to carry out further tests. To ascertain the behaviour which led to or contributed to the deterioration, controlled tests or experiments will need to be carried out in laboratories. An example of laboratory testing and analysis helping to cure a problem is presented in CIOB Technical Information Service Maintenance paper No. 35, *Laboratory analysis as an aid to the diagnosis of rising damp* (Kyte, C.T., 1984).

Rising dampness consists of two basic components: the dampness rising from the ground (*capillary moisture content*) and the hygroscopy of the associated salts (*hygroscopic moisture content*). By analysis of the distribution of these components the presence of rising damp can be confirmed. Its source can be ascertained by chemical analysis, whether from sea water flooding, leaks from tap water, or from soil pipes or kitchen waste, etc. An important feature of moisture movement is the distribution of the water and salts. If water moves from a point x to point y, with an assumption that some will evaporate, a moisture gradient is set up with a high moisture content at x and a lower moisture content at y. If there is any soluble salt present either in the water or in the brickwork then this will be carried in the direction of flow and results in a reverse gradient with a high concentration of salt at y and a low concentration at x. The characteristics of rising damp are the presence of a wet zone at low level, with no significant salt concentration within the wall, and a hygroscopic zone above it with high salt concentrations. In order to determine the type of water in the wall, samples of its constituent chemicals, the hygroscopic moisture and capillary water, need to be taken from the brick wall and sent to a laboratory for analysis. This can show, for example, whether an applied render has failed or whether the DPC is responsible – or both.

Major problems have arisen with a number of concrete system-built dwellings and in order to ascertain the strength of the concrete and its general condition samples are taken and analysed in a laboratory. Increasing use is being made of laboratory facilities in order to test the behaviour and performance of materials.

The purpose of investigation

There are a number of general points that can be made from the aforementioned examples. First, the investigative procedure must be considered with respect to the purpose. In the case of the claddings, the inspection and diagnosis should try to assess whether the construction of fixings, tie backs and supports has overcome inaccuracies without loss of security and durability, and whether joints are within their working limits of size and are likely to remain so. The inspection and diagnosis should take into account that the life of many sealants, even under ideal conditions of use, is usually considerably less than that of the cladding.

The purpose of investigating a crack in brickwork is to ascertain the reason for its appearance. It is assumed that movement has caused it, but this movement needs to be objectively measured and analysed, together with other evidence, to find its cause. The investigation commences with the premise that there is movement in the building. The investigation into the failure may be precautionary as the failure will not be readily apparent. Buildings built to a similar system or constructed around the same time may have shown problems which trigger the investigative process. Depending on the extent of the already known problems the investigation may be limited to remote probes, or to selective removal of parts of the outer leaf. Where the strength or general condition of materials is in doubt or cannot be assessed by inspection, laboratory tests will be required.

Whichever investigative procedure is used, it must be comprehensive, thorough, well recorded and well written-up, with all the evidence presented, and with some indication of the extent of deterioration. A report should contain the following information: (a) the name of the inspector; (b) the weather prior to inspection; (c) sketch plans and elevations as necessary, with orientation; (d) detailed sketches and/or photographs; (e) indications (symptoms), in construction or in performance, such as rain penetration, relative movement, cracking, with dimensions; (f) assessment, with evidence; (g) recommendations for coping with deterioration; and (h) a record of the exact nature of the remedial action taken.

DETERIOROLOGY

There is a growing awareness of a need for a better understanding of performance evaluations to ensure that materials will stand up to long-term exposure conditions. This applies to both new build and repair, where materials are required to last. Dr Roger Browne has put forward some ideas for a new discipline – the science of decay or 'deteriorology'. Its aims are as follows:

1. Encourage the study of deterioration processes.
2. Bring together the wide range of scientific and applied disciplines involved.
3. Survey the performance of existing buildings.
4. Improve the evaluation of general and micro-climatic factors relevant to the deterioration of different materials in service and with age.
5. Evaluate and develop testing techniques both in the laboratory and in the field.

6. Develop design strategies for life prediction.
7. Collate economic strategies for materials selection to aid practitioners' specific needs.
8. Provide a mental focus for training the young professional on how to design and specify for life performance, instead of avoiding the issue.

A number of issues arise from this list. In the first place there is little doubt that these aims are laudable, and that the discipline should be positively encouraged to develop. A range of knowledge and skills would be required in order to realise these aims, such as a scientific appreciation of the behaviour of materials, a knowledge of building construction, and an ability to advise on appropriate choices of materials. Should the person to realise these aims be from a pure science background or from a building technology background? Can one develop from the other to produce a 'deteriorologist'? If a science background is deemed desirable, should this be in physics or in chemistry? Physics might be more appropriate for the examination of such factors as micro-climate, but chemistry might be more relevant for the study of the properties of materials. It is likely that people from all backgrounds can make a contribution to this discipline, but that it will be science-led.

The reasons for the need for 'deteriorology' are numerous and valid. The data that manufacturers provide on products, if available, are not always relevant to particular uses and combinations with other products. As technological change and development is continuous and rapid, products change before long-term experience is gained. In the quest to bring a new product onto the market there are difficulties in relating research results to performance in practice. There is a natural reluctance for state-sponsored laboratories to recommend a particular manufacturer's products. Gaining access to research results from other countries can be time consuming. Textbooks are either too general, or can only concentrate on narrow details. The tests now employed are generally of a short duration and the results cannot be confidently used. Standard tests do not assess the material or product in a real situation and therefore do not give support to performance evaluation. Feedback from performance in use is sparse. Finally, there are very few people with the knowledge and training to cope with the wide range of disciplines involved in assessing performance.

Any initiatives in this field should be supported by all professions and interests in the construction industry. Hopefully the introductory information and notions provided in this volume will kindle interest in the new discipline, and encourage builders and designers to take greater note of current research and development and to incorporate findings into their practice.

SUMMARY

This chapter on deterioration has considered four major aspects: the agencies of decay; the properties of materials in relation to their rates of deterioration; the influence that design and construction decisions and processes have on the rate and influence of deterioration; and, finally, the investigation processes that can be adopted in order to ascertain defects and failures.

There are definite connections between the properties of the material (and its use in a component), the agencies of decay, the initial design solutions specified and the care with which the work is carried out on site. There seems to be very little excuse, with the present state of knowledge and experience available within and without the construction industry, not to be able to predict confidently the performance of a material and component. There is a wealth of scientific evidence on the structure of materials and their characteristics under known conditions. Most of this evidence is available from a wide range of sources, but for reasons which are analysed in *Building Technology 3* its use in determining competent design decisions is scarce. In addition, problems exist on site where levels of quality control can be improved. In many instances the levels of skill are available but carelessness leads to poor construction, which in turn leads to an increased rate of deterioration. When this happens investigation procedures have to be instigated to determine the reasons for the problems so that effective remedial action can be taken.

In theory, if the right material is used, with the degree of protection needed to meet the demands of the environment and if the construction is designed to achieve its optimum performance and built to the specified quality standards, there should be no need for investigative procedures. Of course, there is bound to be some deterioration (referred to as the ageing process) but detailed investigations should not be necessary if the initial choice, design and construction is correct, and meets the user's demands. The British construction industry has to achieve much higher standards in order to reduce the effects of deterioration. Perhaps with the introduction of the British Standard on Quality Assurance a wave of increased consciousness regarding fitness for purpose and quality control will bring about an improvement. The industry can respond when necessary, as the Reading University report comparing the UK with the USA in terms of speed, productivity and cost of building shows. It now seems that the British building industry can match the USA's in terms of productivity, speed of erection and cost. If the will exists, a greater awareness of materials technology can be imparted to all sections of the industry from designer to specifier and from client to operative. The information is on the whole available; it now needs to be widely disseminated, absorbed and utilised by practitioners.

QUESTIONS

1. Describe an investigation procedure that could be used to ascertain the condition of timber window frames.
2. Discuss the value of appraisal procedures for the owner of a major multi-storey office building.
3. Using a building defect recently experienced, discuss the relative influence that the various agencies of deterioration had on its occurrence.
4. Discuss how levels of awareness regarding the use of materials can be effectively raised by those engaged in the process of construction.

Part Three
FIRE TECHNOLOGY

8. Introduction

The subject of fire technology embraces a number of disciplines and areas of knowledge. The concern in this book is with (a) the technology of fire with respect to buildings, (b) the materials of construction, (c) the structure and fabric, (d) the layout of the building, and (e) the behaviour of the people inside the building. Consideration of the technology of fire involves examining the ways in which fires start and spread, and their effect upon a building and its occupants. The attitude of society, as reflected by legislation on safety and insurance, will provide the framework for the physical responses to the risk of fire. Cost, both in monetary terms and in terms of lives, plays a large part in the provision of fire safety measures. Research and development into fire resistance materials and methods of construction, together with effective equipment to prevent or quench fires, is constantly being pursued. Fire technology encompasses the complex but fine details of fire ignition, and the design and construction of whole buildings which can cope with fire and provide adequate protection for the people within. It is also concerned with limiting the scope of a fire to one unit or to a part thereof.

The Great Fire of London in 1666 drew attention to the need for building control as a means of fire containment. Prior to this a London Building Act had been enabled in 1189 in response to a fire in 1136. Fire assurance developed with some rapidity after 1666 and in this connection buildings were inspected with respect to their integrity in fire. It was not until the later 1700s that the provision of structural fire protection was taken seriously, and it was not until the Industrial Revolution, with its massive increase in the numbers of buildings constructed, that worthwhile advances in materials technology took place. Gypsum plaster, concrete and rolled steel enabled the first fireproof structures to be built. In the wake of these developments, control regulations refined the fire provisions, in the form of the Metropolitan Borough Act of 1844 and the London Building Act of 1894. These covered not only the fire resistant nature of buildings but the provision of adequate space between them and of firefighting facilities. A more scientific approach to the problems of fire was given credibility with the establishment of the British Fire Protection Committee at the end of the 1800s. Purpose-built experimental testing huts made a considerable contribution to knowledge of fires. The committee was responsible for an internal congress in London in 1903, which was followed up with attempts to standardise fire resistance tests.

In 1923 a Royal Commission reported on fire prevention (Royal Commission on Fire Brigades and Fire Prevention, Report Cmd, 1945, London, HMSO, 1923), which was soon followed by the publication of British Standard BS 476: 1932, *British Standard Definitions for Fire Resistance, Incombustibility and Non-Flammability of Building Materials and Structures*. This was based on research findings from the USA, Germany and Sweden as well as the UK. A committee set up in 1938 to look at the fire grading of buildings did not report until 1946, owing to the war. In 1947 the Fire Research Station was established at Borehamwood, England, and became part of The Building Research Establishment in 1976. Parallel work on fire protection studies was carried out in the USA, and in 1905 the Americans established a committee for the preparation of fire standards. This committee published a standard specification (C19) for a standard heating curve. This curve was similar to those adopted by Germany, Sweden and the UK and still holds good today.

The major revisions to the UK Building Regulations in 1965, 1976 and 1985 have all incorporated the current developments in fire protection research. Surges in legislation have occurred after major fires, as for example following the Summerland Leisure Centre fire on the Isle of Man in 1973. Statistics maintained from 1946 in the UK suggest that there has been an inexorable trend towards an increase in the number of separate fires, with the largest increase being in fires within dwellings.

There are five main components of fire protection:

1. preventing the initiation of fire
2. restricting the growth and spread of fire
3. containing fire within specified boundaries, whether the whole building or a part thereof
4. providing a means of escape for the occupants of the building
5. controlling fire by automatic devices and by active fire fighting.

When these are considered in relation to (a) design, (b) the nature of fire, (c) the means of passive and active fire precautions, (d) the means of escape, and (e) social attitudes, including approach to fire safety, legislation and insurance, they will comprise the study of fire technology in the subject chapters.

FIRE SAFETY MODELS

Before looking in detail at the components of fire technology, two approaches to the fire safety system, both developed in the USA, will be discussed. One is a logical event 'tree' and the other a computer simulation model.

The Decision Tree

This model was developed by the National Fire Protection Association Systems Concepts Committee for Fire Protection in Structures, in an attempt to develop a concept of fire as a problem consisting of a set of interrelated, interdependent parts. The tree is set out as a simple flow chart diagram, starting with the *Fire Safety Objectives* and branching into two main routes, *Prevent Fire Ignition* and *Manage Fire Impact*. Each box on the tree is an event and a means or method for the higher event to take place. Furthermore, events are connected by either an 'or gate' or an 'and gate'. The former indicates independence; if success is achieved in either event, success will occur in the higher event. The 'and gate' indicates independence; if success is to be achieved in the higher event, all the lower events must be successful. A section of the Decision Tree is shown in Fig. 3.1.

The Decision Tree can be applied as:

(a) a curriculum guide for the study of fire protection

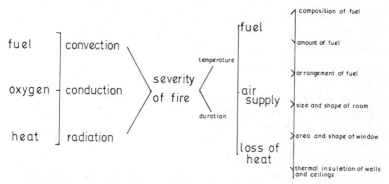

Fig. 3.1 *Factors of fire propagation*

(b) a plan for research in fire protection, and particularly for research organisations in the field of fire technology
(c) a design guide for solving fire protection problems
(d) a basis for establishing building regulations and codes
(e) a means of judging building materials manufacturers' products;
(f) a guide to a building owner to ensure fire safety.

It is theoretically possible to quantity each of the blocks on the Decision Tree. To do this would mean that each event would need a 'probability statement' or a numerical 'standard'. To date, it has not been found possible to quantify confidently every event. If it were possible to give accurate predictions to all events the tree could be a powerful aid in assessing the relative trade-offs to the two main routes, i.e. either to prevent fire ignition or to manage fire impact.

The Building Fire Safety Model

The other systems approach is based on a computer simulation called a Building Fire Safety Model. The model describes the temporal and spatial characteristics of fire development and the associated combustion products of fire. It can also provide a framework for describing the natural, and often unexplained, variations in fire behaviour and can serve as a tool for investigating the effects of actions that might alter the fire environment. The model is confined to small dwellings and is divided into 'realms' matching the critical stages in fire development. These realms are measurable, by such criterion as flame height, heat release rate and upper room-air temperature. The development of a fire may not pass through all consecutive realms. Realms may be 'jumped', as, for example, where extension of the fire is considered to be at least as important as the severity of the fire in the room of origin. The boundaries of the realms have not been accurately defined and one can easily run into another. The realms are listed as:

Realm 1	preburning
Realm 2	sustained burning
Realm 3	vigorous burning
Realm 4	interactive burning
Realm 5	remote burning
Realm 6	room involvement
Realm 7	flame spread.

The model provides a tool for assessing the expected characteristics of fire development. Transition probability values are given to the development of the fire from one realm to another when set in a known series of constraints and events, for example, a fire in a living-room settee with specified materials in the furniture and fabric. A simulation of the most likely fire scenarios for a range of occupancy uses, interior finishes and furniture can be employed as a quantitative assessment of the safety of a particular building design. A 'hazard profile' can be produced which can be compared to other designs.

Conclusion

The two systems described show approaches to the problem of achieving safety in buildings from the effect of fire. These systems were put forward in the 1970s, and in Chapters 7 and 8 a further discussion will analyse their value in the light of developments in fire technology in the late 1980s. For now, they illustrate that the basis of understanding fire and providing buildings that mitigate its effect depends upon a wide range of knowledge fields, including computer science, physics, chemistry, statistics and logic. They are a product of the need to create knowledge-based systems for fire safety in buildings.

In the following chapters the constituent aspects of fire technology and its application will be discussed. Chapter 9 will consider the role of the building's designer and the type and scope of approaches that ought to be taken in designing to reduce fire risk. The nature of fire itself will be described in Chapter 10, along with how materials ignite and what happens in a fire. Chapters 11 and 12 will consider the means available to protect the building and to manage a fire. Perhaps the most important aspect of fire safety is to ensure the safe egress of people from the area of a fire, and with this in mind, Chapter 13 looks at means of escape. There is a need to view fire safety from a knowledgeable scientific and technological stance, and in Chapter 14 the concept of fire safety engineering is presented. This is followed by a discussion of all aspects of fire technology, its effect on such matters as fire insurance, and future developments in legislation and approaches to fire safety. In this final chapter the report by Malhotra, *Fire safety in buildings*, will be analysed and considered in respect to the foregoing chapters.

QUESTIONS

1. Surges in interest in fire protection measures have followed major fires leading to loss of life. Should progress be made only at the expense of human life?
2. Discuss the value of using the Decision Tree as a means of assessing the risk of fire in a building. Compare it with the use of the computer simulation.

9. Design of Buildings

In this chapter the problems of designing buildings with respect to providing fire protection and means of escape will be weighed against those of other factors of design such as space and circulation, weather resistance and security. But first the responsibility of the architect with respect to fire is outlined.

THE ARCHITECT'S RESPONSIBILITY

A client's brief is unlikely to spell out his needs for fire safety or means of escape although he may mention particular hazards – to do with the user's requirements – that can increase fire risk (or produce toxic fumes). It is the designer's responsibility to ensure that all statutory codes and regulations are applied and put into operation at the time of practical completion. In the initial feasibility study the fire regulations must be considered, as they will influence the design and layout of the building and make an impact on cost. Incorporated into the feasibility study should be a life cycle costing exercise. The total costs of a building throughout its planned life should be estimated. One of these annually recurring costs will be insurance of the building, which will cover fire. The premiums are to be taken into account assuming the provision of fire protection measures. The installation of automatic fire fighting equipment such as sprinklers could lead to an appreciable reduction in premium when compared to a building without sprinklers. If this saving is totalled over the life of the building it could provide a large contribution to the capital cost of providing the sprinklers. This does not necessarily consider the actual cost of a fire, in terms of the provision of alternative accommodation, nor the factor of injury or loss of life; it is virtually impossible to calculate this, although courts of law do assess damages in cases of proven negligence or criminal practice leading to fires. If these costs were taken into consideration, the actual cost of providing active automatic fire equipment could be quite low.

The designer must bring together all the relevant information, in the form of acts, by-laws, standards, codes of practice and regulations appertaining to the fire safety of buildings. The local fire prevention officer needs to be consulted, in conjunction with the local Building Control Officer. In the light of the aspect of insurance mentioned above, the building client's insurance company will also be consulted. Insurance companies in the UK follow a set of rules produced by the Fire Officers' Committee. Most fire insurance companies are members of the Committee, and its rules form the basis for calculating insurance premiums for all types of buildings. These are constantly amended in the light of the latest research, regulations, British Standards and Codes of Practice. The regulations, standards and codes of practice are only minimum requirements, and individual clients, or buildings at high risk, may require fire safety measures over and above the norm. This can be reflected in the quotation of high rates of premiums.

W. Allen has put forward some ideas on how an architect ought to make provision for fire resistance in the design process ('How the architect views provision for fire resistance', in *Proceedings: Fire-resistance requirements for buildings – a new approach*, Department of the Environment and Fire Officers' Committee Joint Fire Research Organisation, HMSO 1973). The architect ought to draw on scientific knowledge to find a basis for balanced action, and a systems approach ought to be adopted. Architects need to know which are constant factors and which are variables in the trade-offs between all the factors in fire safety and the other design factors. Allen advocates the use of performance specifications as an alternative to what might be seen as arbitrary requirements set in tablets of stone. Research and development can best be utilised when performance criteria are specified. Allen advocates a positive approach to information on fire safety: instead of saying what *can* be done it might be better to set positive *goals*. The use of mathematics and computers is seen to be alien to the practice of architecture, but perhaps pertinent software (such as the Building Fire Safety Model) could aid architects.

Allen suggests that architects ought to cultivate a thorough understanding of how fires commence, develop and spread in buildings, and how their toxic influence accompanies this spread (the majority of deaths in fires are a result of the inhalation of smoke and toxic fumes). They should consider, moreover, how a general understanding might relate to any particular design problem in the course of solution. They should be aware of probable risks and be familiar with the passive and active measures that can be used to exercise control, give protection and assist fire fighting, as well as the kinds of provision that can be made to ensure that people escape safely.

In *Fire and Building: a guide for the design team* (Collins, 1984) the Aqua Group has provided a list of items in a loose order of priority which will aid designers in establishing criteria for assessing fire protection requirements:

(a) *Purpose group* and *occupancy group* as defined in Approved Document B and the 'Means of Escape in Case of Fire' mandatory document in the Building Regulations 1985
(b) *Location of building*: and associated risks
(c) *Size of building*: regulations and circumstances requiring special provision
(d) *Construction*: influencing factors and areas of decision
(e) *Internal planning*: the brief and its consequences
(f) *Special storage facilities*: risks and provisions
(g) *Special parking requirements*: impact of planning on services and safety
(h) *Fire protection requirements*: provision to be made
(i) *Mechanical services*: degree of isolation and protection.

COST CRITERIA

The question of cost is nearly always of paramount importance at the design stage and some general rules apply. For instance, the larger the size of the compartment, the greater the hazard, the higher the standard of fire resistance required (both for the compartment and the building structure), the greater the cost, and the more onerous the insurance premiums. The optimisation of compartment layout may influence the building form. The smaller the volume, the less the fire load, which means that the fire rating of the structural elements can be reduced, leading to a decrease in costs. This has to be weighed against the costs of forming the compartment walls.

There are a number of criteria with cost implications which need to be assessed by the designers:

(a) *Location on site*: the position of the building relative to adjacent structures and to site boundary with corresponding impact on compartmentation, daylight and fenestration. Areas in the building will be subject to a client's demands regarding the configuration of lettable space and market rates with subsequent returns on investment on commercial property.
(b) *Building height*: affects compartmentation, escape routes and fire rating of structure. The taller the building, the higher these costs.
(c) *Pattern of tenancy*. The best use of lettable floor space may conflict with the need to provide party walls. The necessity of shared entrances or staircases must also be considered.
(d) *Escape routes*. The width and number of escape routes are related to the building's use and can affect the number of people able to use each floor. Factors such as travel distance, sub-division of floors and dead-ends can influence floor shape.

(e) *Structural element*: whether a building is constructed in heavyweight or lightweight, built in traditional or newly developed materials. A higher speed of erection to produce early return on investment can lead to higher costs in achieving fire rating.

(f) *Fabric*. The external fabric will be subject to aesthetic considerations, but also to the need to meet fire resistance standards. The fire resistance criterion needs to interrelate with thermal performance, weathertightness and durability criteria. The surface spread of flame and the location and size of windows related to cill heights and daylight factors need to be balanced.

(g) *Roof*. Roof materials and methods of construction need to meet fire resistance standards as well as thermal, access, maintenance and interstitial condensation criteria. The roof may provide a means of escape.

(h) *Security*. Surveillance, detection and alarm systems can be linked with fire safety measures to give economic benefits.

(i) *Automatic fire prevention*. Automatic systems like the sprinkler system are costly but may be necessary depending on the use of the building. They can allow larger compartments and greater flexibility in the use of space, also giving benefits in lower insurance premiums.

(j) *Smoke exhaust systems*. These are required in certain types of buildings with particular kinds of uses and can affect the building form, the number and design of escape routes and staircases, minimising them and thereby holding down costs.

The costs involved in providing fire safety measures in refurbishment work are generally higher than those for new work. In refurbishment and alteration work the whole building will have to comply with the relevant statutory codes even though the works may be confined to a small area or a floor. To provide fire resistance measures and escape routes in existing structures can create complex design problems whose solutions are generally labour-intensive, meaning that implementation will be costly. In the case of historic buildings it may not be possible to meet current requirements without destroying the preserved character. Compromises may need to be negotiated with the statutory officers to best meet the fire safety requirements while still preserving the original building fabric.

INFLUENCES ON FIRE SAFETY MEASURES

In designing a building, fire safety is but one of a number of functions which interrelate to meet the client's brief. Other functions included are space and circulation, daylighting, loading and structural design, weather resistance, thermal and sound insulation, services, security and durability and maintenance. These are now considered in relation to their compatibility and influence over fire safety measures.

Space and circulation

Around buildings the three main considerations are: (a) the spacing of buildings in relation to their site boundaries to reduce hazard; (b) the spacing of buildings to reduce the risk of fire penetration through the roof of a building from an external source; and (c) the spacing of buildings to ensure adequate access facilities for the fire brigade.

Within buildings, the larger the space, the greater the potential fire area, the greater the potential fire risk and the greater the likely losses should a fire occur. Internal heights should not be overlooked, as the effective response times of active fire fighting measures change according to the height of the device above the floor. Circulation spaces, corridors and staircases provide no profit to building investors, so a balance needs to be struck between eliminating excessive and wasteful circulation space and meeting the fire safety requirements.

Daylighting

The use of materials to allow adequate daylight into the building must be related to their fire function. Only wired glass gives some measure of fire protection by retaining its integrity and reducing radiated heat transmission by 50%. Generally, the thicker the glass, the greater the reduction in radiated heat. Plastic can be used in roof lights in accordance with the Building Regulations 1985 Approved Document B. The overall size and cill height of the window needs to be considered with respect to both internal natural lighting requirements and criteria governing the spread of flame.

Loading and structural design

Structurally, a building is designed to cater for all superimposed and dead loads. Each floor, or part of a building, must not lead to progressive collapse if that particular part fails. This could occur in a fire when a floor collapses, spilling its materials and contents on to a floor below. It is important to ensure that a continuity of fire resistance is maintained throughout the load-bearing elements and in certain cases where the integrity of a compartment is dependent upon unprotected steelwork, discontinuity of the structural frame may well be a vital factor in maintaining the structural stability. This needs to be considered where large spans and/or complex space frames are used. With the advent of recently developed applied materials, lightweight structures in steel can now meet fire requirements and give economic benefits in terms of reduced foundations and lightweight claddings.

Weather-tightness

The method and type of cladding used must satisfy both fire and weather resistance functions. Problems can arise with a cladding's fixings in the case of fire: they can be badly affected, leading to distortion and failure of the joints, allowing the ingress of rain, etc. This might also lead to dislodgement of the cladding if not remedied. Materials and construction details which produce viable weather-tightness may not always provide suitable fire resistance. Most roofing materials provide adequate fire resistance, with the exception of some built-up bitumen felt constructions which may give only limited protection. Plastic sheets provide poor resistance to fire and to the spread of flame.

Thermal and sound insulation

A common solution to the ever-increasing demands for both thermal and sound insulation (see Part Two, p.55) is the insertion of quilts, bats, foam or loose granules into walls and roofs. These materials must prevent the spread of flame. Materials such as bricks, blocks and concrete will give enhanced thermal and sound insulation through an increase in thickness, which will also increase their ability to withstand fire. Insulation for buildings with service pipes and ducts located externally must satisfy fire, thermal, weather resistance, security and durability criteria.

Services

These installations can be the potential source of fires and may be the means by which fire can spread.

Artificial lighting is required in all buildings, and public buildings need an emergency power source to allow egress in the case of a fire cutting the main electricity source. Secondary lighting needs to be provided in all corridors, staircases and exits forming escape routes. The main lighting fittings themselves can be fire risks, as can cable installations. Electrically powered motors, for lifts for example, can cause fires and must be well protected.

Heating plant and methods of circulation need to be considered in relation to their fire risks. For example, a boiler-room should be well protected structurally, have smoke exhausts and some means of preventing or fighting any fire which may occur. Any fuel shortage problem needs careful consideration and must be solved in order to comply with current regulations.

Mechanical ventilation and air conditioning systems may provide routes for the spread of fire and smoke. In the Building Regulations 1985 the spread of smoke is specifically mentioned for the first time. The spread of smoke must be prevented, so the design of any air circulation system must be carried out with the fire safety factors foremost in mind.

In the case of tall or particularly large commercial or public buildings, an adequate supply of water, to the optimum pressure, should be available. Additional water storage may be required to meet the demands of fire fighting, as in the case of a sprinkler system.

Security

Unfortunately there is sometimes a conflict between ensuring adequate free egress from a building in case of fire, and providing security against unlawful ingress. A typical example is the provision of unlocked outward opening doors on to a public highway from a theatre. There have been too many instances of fire escape doors being padlocked, preventing escape and causing unnecessary loss of life. Door systems have been developed which can provide both good security and easy egress. The problem lies in the management of the buildings. The usage patterns and management of a building are vital components of fire technology and the designer should give them detailed consideration (see Chapters 14 and 15).

Durability and maintenance

No fire resistance measures or means of escape provision should unduly decrease the durability or contribute excessively to the maintenance of a building. The provisions themselves should be durable, too, and require a minimum of maintenance. Fire fighting equipment, however, should be frequently checked and tested, as should escape routes.

FIRE SAFETY RULES

In rounding off this chapter on design in relation to fire, further mention should be made of the Rules of the Fire Officers' Committee. This committee has now been disbanded, but its technical works still continue under the administration of the Loss Prevention Council. Its findings and recommendations are published in five booklets. From time to time reissues, amendments, addenda, approved lists and further recommendations are published.

Rules for Construction of Buildings: Standards I–V

The general effect of these rules is to divide a building into fire compartments, with the aim of reducing the total area at risk. Limiting the area of a fire means that the development of heat is restricted, with less risk of the fire spreading and also making it more easy to fight. Its spread into other parts of the same building is also restricted at the same time. Standard I sets the most stringent standards, while Standard V sets the least stringent. A building which fails to meet the last standard is regarded as 'non-standard'. In practice a small construction amendment can change a building from one standard to another, by an increase in wall thickness or the elimination of a door fan-light, for example. There may be no correlation between an FOC Standard and a statutory requirement. Each must be checked independently – and both conditions met.

Rules for the Construction of Buildings: Grades 1 and 2

These grades are related to the use to which a building is put. Generally, Grade 1 defines a building of non-combustible and fire resisting construction based on predicted two-hour fire resistance. Grade 2 defines non-combustible construction based on predicted half-hour fire resistance.

Rules for automatic sprinkler installations

Statutes may demand the installation of sprinklers in certain buildings, but fire insurance cover may be virtually impossible in other buildings deemed to be at risk by the FOC. A large discount on premiums could repay the capital outlay within a period of five years. The installation must provide: *detection, warning, containment* and, in some cases, *extinguishment*. The statutory rules specify the minimum standards required for the installation of sprinklers in buildings under three classifications: 'extra light hazard'; 'ordinary hazard' and 'extra high hazard'. In considering the installation of sprinklers the designer should look at:

(a) legal requirements
(b) FOC requirements
(c) insurers' requirements
(d) the availability of water supply at the right pressure and flow rate
(e) the effect of the saving on the fire insurance premium related to building structure, plant, raw material stock, manufactured stock and the consequential loss policy
(f) the possibility of writing-off the cost of installation against profits in the first year after installation
(g) the effect of an extension or alteration to an existing building.

Rules for automatic fire alarm installation

These rules relate to equipment such as smoke- and heat-detectors and embrace such matters as definitions, classification of installation, areas to be protected, siting and spacing, apparatus, location, power supplies, wiring and connection, testing and maintenance. The FOC provides a list of approved automatic sprinkler and automatic fire alarm systems.

Rules for construction and installation of firebreak doors, lobbies and shutters

There are four sections to these rules. Section 1 deals with a specification for doors and shutters in the following categories: (a) iron or steel doors; (b) metal-covered doors and (c) steel rolling shutters. The specifications give requirements for the construction of door, hinges, pivots and frame. Section 2 provides a list of approved manufacturers of types of doors, listing the FOC reference number, the type of construction and fixing and the maximum size of wall opening. Section 3 gives a specification for the construction of firebreak lobbies. Section 4 refers to shutter protection to windows or other similar openings in external walls, and their specification related to Sections 1 and 2.

CONCLUSION

Insurers of buildings use statutory rules and procedures to assess a building for fire insurance purposes. A designer should be aware of these procedures and be satisfied that the design process fully considers all aspects relating to fire.

The design of buildings to reduce the propagation of fire, and to contain incipient fires, involves three areas of concern:

1. the materials used in the interior finish of the building
2. the prompt detection of the incipient fire
3. the effective suppression of the fire.

The designer has full control over these aspects of a building's construction. Different materials have different characteristics in terms of flame spread, smoke production and rate of heat release. The geometric configuration of a building affects fire propagation, as do the arrangement, types and configuration of the furnishings and decorative materials. In the next chapter a review of the nature of fire is presented.

QUESTIONS

1. At which stages and in how much detail should fire safety measures be integrated into the designing of a building?
2. Discuss the difficulties involved in designing and constructing for fire safety in refurbishment work.
3. Discuss the significance of the Fire Officers' Committee's Rules on the design of buildings.
4. Review the Building Regulations 1985 with respect to their view on the provision of fire resistance and means of escape.

10. Fire!

THE NATURE OF FIRE

Fire is the process of burning, and requires three essential ingredients: *a combustible substance*, *heat* and *oxygen*. In the absence of any one of these a fire will cease. There must be an appropriate relationship between the three ingredients: with two in balance the introduction of the third ingredient can create incipient fire.

The behaviour of fires varies markedly(there are 'hot' fires, 'quick' fires, 'smoky' fires, 'smouldering' fires and 'slow' fires. One determinant of a fire's behaviour is the chemical composition of the combustible substance, together with its bulk. The principles of fire propagation apply to fires in both solids and liquids, but their subsequent behaviour once alight can be very different. Gaseous emissions will occur much more readily from liquids than from the majority of solid materials, and with the application of far less heat. Those liquids which can vaporize at room temperatures are said to have low flash points. When the vapour is free to mix with the oxygen in the air only a small amount of heat is needed to start a fire in the vapour cloud, thus the risk of explosion can be very high.

Heat can come from a flame, from a glowing source (such as a cigarette) or a spark, from friction or from electricity. Also the general raising of temperature to very high levels can spontaneously start a fire. Heat energy is transmitted by one or more of the three following means:

1. *Conduction*: the transfer of heat through a solid material from a region of high temperature to a region of lower temperature.
2. *Convection*: the transfer of heat in or by a liquid or a gas by the movement of the medium.
3. *Radiation*: the transfer of heat through a gas or vacuum other than by heating of the intervening space.

Fire is a particularly complex phenomenon, however, so some further explanation is necessary.

Ignition

Ignition occurs within the gases evolved when solids or liquids are heated. Radiation or hot gases may start a fire in a different part of a room or building from that in which they are formed. If insufficient oxygen is available in a room with a window some of the fuel (after the heat has broken the glass) will burn outside. When heat falls on a piece of material, some of it is absorbed and conducted into the body of that material. The heat on the surface then raises the surface temperature. The surface will warm up more quickly if it is poor conductor such as wood, which requires a surface temperature of 300°C before sufficient vapours are released for ignition, at which point a small flame will ignite. In the absence of a small flame the gases need to reach a temperature of about 500°C before spontaneous combustion occurs.

A fire starting in the corner of a room may take the following course: 1. The floor under the burning materials will become heated by conduction. 2. The ceiling immediately above the burning materials and some distance away will become heated by convection. 3. Convection currents, travelling at a speed of one or two metres per second, will heat materials a long way from the fire. 4. Near to the fire other combustible materials around the burning area will be heated by radiation from the flames. The relative importance of the processes of heat transfer will change according to the situation and stage of the fire.

The time taken to ignite a material depends very strongly on its thermal properties, as these govern the rate of heat build-up. Ignition can be delayed by the chemical composition of the material. For example, by promoting decomposition at lower temperatures than normal the volatiles will not normally ignite because they have not reached the temperature necessary for ignition, and when the material does become hot enough the volatiles have been partially exhausted.

Flame and fire spread

Fire can spread by three means: first, along a continuous combustible surface; second, through a continuous bed of fuel; and third, through a discontinuous bed of fuel. Two main questions need to be asked regarding a possible fire in a building. *Will it spread?* And, if so, *how quickly?*

Flame spreading along a continuous surface will move both horizontally and vertically. If the material is thin, then convection in the vertical direction can play a large part in heating unburnt fuel above the burning area. This leads to further ignition when enough volatiles have been released fast enough to sustain the flame and thereby extend the burning area. The weight per unit area of the fuel is the main influence on the rate of flame-spread in thin materials. With an increase in thickness there will need to be a consequent increase in temperature to maintain the rate of flame-spread. This is inversely proportional to the width of a burning marterial, but in relation to its height; it will increase the rate of flame with an increase in width.

Horizontal progression of flame on a thin material will be less rapid than vertical progression because more of the heat is convected away from the unburnt fuel ahead of the fire front. While conduction normally plays no part in fire-spread in thin materials, it is an important factor in relation to combustible building materials as it draws heat into the interior of the materials. If the burning material is a good insulator, heat will be lost to the interior by conduction, and spread across its surface will be slow. But a good insulator will conduct heat away from the burning area more slowly and the spread of flame will be quicker. The thermal properties of combustible board or sheet materials can affect their behaviour in fire relating to the spread of flame. Combustible wall linings in a small room are likely to be quickly affected and spread the fire, as the chance of fire occurring adjacent to the wall is higher than in a large room.

Fire travelling from floor to ceiling, across a combustible wall surface, is an example of spread through a continuous bed of fuel. The lower the bulk density of the material, the less heat is required to burn a unit volume and the faster will be the rate of flame spread.

Fire spreading through discontinuous beds of fuel can lead to extensive fire damage resulting in massive material and financial losses, especially in single-storey industrial building fires. Take the example of a high stack of burning material where the flames are touching the ceiling. At this point an increase in the rate of burning occurs leading to larger flames, which if they cannot go upwards will deflect along the ceiling and increase in length. This is because the mixing of air and fuel in the flame is more difficult when cold air has to rise against gravity than when it is deflected sideways into a vertical flame. The weaker, deflected flame is longer, and in the right position can heat the ceiling which itself radiates downwards supplementing the flame radiation. These flames can easily affect combustible materials some way from the fire's source and the chance of the fire propagating is increased by a factor of five.

Steady combustion

Growth of a fire often accelerates until it is stopped, and there can be an identifiable moment when all combustible surfaces contribute to burning; this is generally known as 'flashover'. Flashover occurs when a developing fire reaches a level of activity at which the gases already emitted will suddenly ignite and produce flaming across the surfaces of the pre-heated adjoining combustible materials.

Statistics show that the majority of fires commence with the contents of a building, such as furniture or stored items. These provide the major source of fuel for a fire. Furniture can burn with intense rapidity and the products of combustion are quickly released in the form of smoke and toxic gases. The items at most risk are bedding and upholstery. The use of polymers as materials can cause problems even though their initial ignition may take longer to occur than it does in natural fibres. Once ignited, polymers can burn rapidly and quickly decompose, exposing interior material to the fire. The toxic effect of their emitted gases can impair human physical and mental performance, and exposure to *hot* toxic gases can cause death within a few moments. Smoke and gases can spread a long distance from the seat of a fire, and can therefore affect the whole of the building and all of its occupants.

A building's contents are the largest contributors to fire, but the designer and builder have little control over their choice. It is only in the choice of fabric for the building that initial control can be exercised. For this a knowledge of differing materials is essential, with their differing levels of fire resistance. Experimental work carried out in the USA and UK has established a connection between fire severity and materials. On the basis of furnace tests a temperature/time relationship has been determined for the fire grading of structures. After flashover the severity of a fire is greatly influenced by the amount of fuel available. This can be measured as a total calorific value, known as its 'fire load'. When expressed in heat units per unit of floor area it is known as its 'fire load density', measured in kg/m^2. Internationally recognisable tests have been formulated to check the temperature/time relationship, and the curves produced are virtually the same the world over.

FIRE GRADING

In the broadest sense, fire grading can be defined as the embracing of fire precautions of all kinds to achieve the standards of safety appropriate to the fire hazard of a building. Commonly, the term is confined to the fire resistance of structures. The size and type of fire load are not the only factors that affect the severity of a fire, however: it is also influenced by the design of a building. The design of a building will determine its air supply and the measures taken to prevent heat loss (the use of insulation or materials of low thermal transmittance). These will interact with fire load and affect fire spread and resistance. Tests on small-scale models have found that the heat transfer process in a real fire is very different from that in furnace tests, because the luminous flames of actual fires give greater heat transfer in the early stages. Therefore, even if the temperature/time curves of actual fires and furnace test fires are similar – which they very seldom are – it is not possible to equate fire duration to fire resistance time.

Ventilation is an important factor in controlling fire severity. When windows in a compartment are small an increase in window area or height leads to an increase in burning rate, and consequently to a decrease in the duration of the fire. For the majority of normal fenestrations the duration is proportional to the fire load per unit of window area. When the window is sufficiently large relative to the fire load, the burning rate depends on the fuel itself and is virtually independent of the window area or its surface area thickness. Amount of fuel is here the important burning rate factor. The type and distribution of the fire load, the size and shape of compartments and the amount of heat loss through walls, floors and roofs must therefore be considered to produce a confident prediction for a fire grading.

The factors affecting fire propagation are summarised in Fig. 3.1. *Convection* and *conduction* have already been mentioned, but the spread of fire by *radiation*, discussed now, is the primary method of fire propagation. There is often no visible effect of heating by radiation until dangerous conditions have been attained, whereas convection is visible in the form of flames, smoke and flying brands. Ignition of distant material is often caused by radiation, coupled with a small fire brand or spark. The intensity of radiation from a fire is sensitive to temperature changes within it: an increase in temperature from 900°C to 1100°C virtually doubles the intensity of radiation. The temperature depends upon the balance between the heat lost through the fabric, the heat supplied by the fire and the heat fed back to maintain the fire. In turn, the heat supply depends on the rate of burning and the amount of combustible material. But as ventilation conditions limit the upper rate of burning, an increase in fire load above a certain value does not increase the temperature but leads instead to an increase in fire duration. This time factor has important implications for fire resistance.

The intensity of radiation from a room can be calculated, and then related to the extent of the fire. A fire throughout a whole building will radiate from all the openings in the external walls. If the building has adequate fire resistance in its walls, and if its openings are protected, then the fire should remain contained within the compartments. Experience has shown that flames and radiation can spread over a façade and the wind can then play its part in spreading the fire. The known behaviour of radiation from a burning building is used to determine the interrelationship of space separation between buildings, planning controls, and the fire resistance of external walls. The outer face of a building can provide a direct route for flames from one part of a building to another. This is dependent upon the response of the cladding materials to heat and flame, and the ability of the flames to reach from one opening to another. Although concrete is not combustible, panels can expand due to the heat acting on the steel reinforcement, making the concrete spall and split or even buckle. Fixings can distort or fail, and the cladding fall. Flames will not be deterred from leaping from one opening to another by non-combustible cladding. The most effective preventive measure against this is to ensure adequate distances between openings. Where natural lighting is required, however, this may be virtually impossible.

Within a building, if there is adequate fuel and if ignition has taken place, then a fire will invade all possible spaces. Hot smoke and gases form the vanguard of a fire; as they have a thermal bouyancy, they will build up atmospheric pressure beyond the norm in a confined space. In a duct or lobby this pressure can force smoke and gases through small apertures around doors or pipes into adjoining spaces. A micro-climate can be created in a relatively large space which consists of a higher pressure zone of hot smoke and gases creating air circulation. This pushes lethal clouds vertically and horizontally into the uncontaminated lower pressure zones and at a rapid speed. Vertical spaces, such as stairwells, and horizontal spaces such as corridors, must be considered as flues. The vertical flue effect can be diminished by creating separations at each floor, while horizontal flues can be destroyed by the erection of fire resisting doors. In corridors, flashover or smoke explosion can occur. In the case of multi-storey buildings, fire tends to engulf a complete floor before progressing to the next.

A large problem is to be found in the use of suspended ceilings, for a number of reasons. They form a trap for hot combustion products; they often contain electrical and other services which may be a source of fire; they are sometimes formed of combustible insulations; if insulated, they may encourage the rapid build-up of heat; they can link the extremities of large areas, or of adjoining areas via service installations; they provide ideal conditions for flashover to occur, and, finally, they can conceal the true cause or path of a fire.

In very large spaces such as superstores and shopping malls the stratification of smoke and gas occurs as the products of combustion rise to the ceiling and expand sideways. In so doing they cool until they reach the farthest walls where they fall and are then drawn back towards the fire as it draws in air. This results in layers of smoke moving in opposite directions at different temperatures.

This chapter has described the essential ingredients of fire in relation to a building. The way that fire propogates via radiation, convection and conduction has been discussed, with their resulting effects on the spread of fire. In the understanding of the principles of fire the concepts of fire resistance and means of escape have evolved and it is with the manner in which a building can prevent, contain or quench fire that the next two chapters will be concerned.

QUESTIONS

1. Compare the development of (a) a fire in a small room with one small window and (b) a fire in a large room with a number of big windows.
2. Outline the factors affecting fire severity, and the conditions that can lead to its maximum levels.

11. Passive Fire Protection

In this chapter the means by which the building, its structure, fabric and installations resist the effects of fire will be discussed. Although an integral part of a fire protection strategy, means of escape will be considered in Chapter 13. The issues of this chapter are here discussed with respect to (a) fire hazard, (b) fire resistance, (c) materials, (d) compartmentation, (e) ventilation, (f) control of smoke, (g) hidden spaces, and (h) workmanship.

FIRE HAZARD

In the first place it is necessary to ascertain the fire hazard of a building; as stated in the previous chapter this is measured as the *fire load density*. This can be applied to types of buildings according to their use. Two aspects need to be considered: first, the risk to human life, and, second, the damage to a building. It may be that buildings with few occupants have the highest fire risk owing to the materials contained within them. The prime consideration is the hazard with respect to life, however, and the Building Regulations are based upon this fundamental rationale. Approved Document B (part of the Building Regulations 1985) states the classifications of buildings with respect to their fire hazard as named 'Purpose Groups'. From this initial sub-division the particular requirements relating to structure (or parts thereof) can be ascertained. Guidance is given in the form of examples of good practice. A factor also taken into consideration in assessing risk to life is the familiarity of a building to its users. A hotel is likely to be totally unfamiliar to its overnight users and, similarly, a store in a town centre development needs to be assumed as unfamiliar to its clientele.

The size of the buildings can affect the fire hazard. A large open building can be more vulnerable than a number of small, enclosed, adjoining areas. The height, area (and therefore volume) related to the use or occupancy of the building is a limiting factor in the determination of fire resistance. A tall building can pose a large fire risk, as well as the problems of providing a satisfactory means of escape for its occupants. It can act as a massive flue and enable fire to spread quickly. Warehouses using mechanical stacking methods reaching up to and above the normal two storeys may have a large cubic capacity, this in itself being a contribution to the fire hazard. If a building has a number of separate groups of users or occupants the fire hazard can be increased. A high-risk user will dictate the fire resistance requirements for the whole building.

FIRE RESISTANCE

Tests for fire resistance are used for three main purposes:

1. to assess the actual fire resistance of a construction for regulation recognition
2. to help the development of new products
3. to establish behaviour prediction parameters for greater understanding.

In setting up tests on materials or construction systems the correspondence to actual in-use conditions should be as high as possible. The elements of a building must be treated as integrated, and their boundary conditions have an important influence on their ultimate behaviour in a fire. The stresses and strains of interaction need to be considered, as well as the important factor of the level and method of loading. These test conditions should comply with the maxima provided in the relevant codes of practice. During tests the loads applied need to be kept constant.

The criteria for assessing the performance of construction systems are based on the premise that the way different elements of the construction perform in fire are clearly defined. For example the use of compartments and fire-breaks is seen to be an element of the construction system. The three performance criteria are expressed as the limit-state concepts of:

(a) *stability*: the limit state is reached when the specimen collapses or unacceptable deformation occurs.
(b) *integrity*: the limit state is reached when cracks or other openings exist in a separating element through which flame or hot gases can pass which are capable of igniting a combustible material on the unexposed side.
(c) *insulation*: the limit state is reached when heat transfer through the construction raises the unexposed face temperature to a level considered unsafe for combustible materials in contact with the face.

Malhotra has identified four methods of specifying fire resistance requirements (see Malhotra, H.L., *Design of fire resisting structures*, Surrey University Press, 1982). The flow chart shown in Fig. 3.2 details these methods, of which an explanation follows.

Method 1 illustrates the current position in most countries where empirical fire resistance requirements are satisfied by the

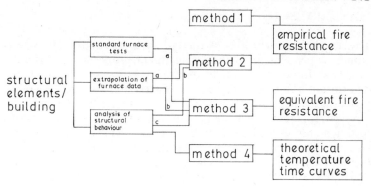

Fig. 3.2   *Methods of providing fire resistance*

conducting of standard fire resistance tests or by the use of (a) relevant standards, (b) known suitable constructions, or (c) codes of practice. In Method 2, two alternatives follow a 'tradition pattern' for the specification of fire resistance. 2a represents the simpler approach of using interpolation/extrapolation techniques to extend the available fire resistance data, and 2b introduces the concept of analysing the structural behaviour of individual elements. The employment of Method 3 is based on a knowledge of the combustible contents of the building and its other characteristics, such as compartment size, windows and construction. Three routes are available for the purposes of compliance: 3a – direct test data; 3b – interpolation techniques; 3c – analysis of structural behaviour. The highest sophistication possible utilises the theoretically determined temperature/time relationships in addition to an analysis of structural performance from first principles using data on material properties and behavioural models for materials and structures; this is shown as Method 4. So far this latter approach has been confined to the analysis of individual elements, but it is hoped that it will be developed to cover the building as a whole.

The most common approach is Method 1, although 2a is gaining a degree of acceptance. Some countries have recognised 2b. Methods 3a and 3b have been occasionally used but only as a means to give relaxation to standard requirements. If 3a does become acceptable it is likely that recognition of 3c will follow. A considerable amount of development work is currently being carried out on Method 4.

MATERIALS

The manner in which construction systems respond to fire is mainly dependent upon their constituent properties. Brief mention has already been made of fire as a possible factor in the deterioration of materials (see Part Two of this volume). The four properties which can affect behaviour in fire are (a) chemical, (b) physical, (c) mechanical and (d) thermal. One problem involved in testing materials as they might be affected in a fire, is that fire is a transient situation, rather than a steady state. Extensive tests have been carried out on concrete, steel, masonry and timber, however, and much knowledge has been gained about their behaviour in fire.

Fire resistance needs to be calculated, in order to predict the behaviour of a structural element, in tests – which may or may not simulate actual fire conditions. The fire resistance is computed by working through the following broad stages. 1. *Define heat exposure* (this is based on codes, regulations relating to the building, and an assessment of fire severity due to fire load, ventilation and compartment characteristics). 2. *Determine effect of heat on structure* (this requires calculation of the heat transfer based on thermal expansion, temperature field, stresses, loss of strength and an estimation of the physical damage). 3. *Determine reduction of load-bearing capacity*. When residual strength is compared to the design load, there may be a need to increase or redesign the protection; this can be reflected in the initial definition of the structural design and this might loop back into the determination of reduction in load-bearing capacity. When residual strength exceeds the design load the fire resistance can be regarded as adequate.

Taking the example of concrete, the process and factors considered in its design will be considered, with particular reference to ensuring fire resistance. In most cases compliance with CP 110 will give exemptions under most load conditions as well as giving adequate fire resistance properties for periods of up to two hours.

The two main types of concrete structural elements are *flexural members* (beams and floors) and *compression members* (columns and walls). There is far more information available on flexural members than on compression members. In the first instance the exposure conditions of the particular members, or interconnected members, need to be ascertained. Factors such as support, restraint, slenderness and thickness will affect their behaviour in a fire. Also, whether a member has one face or a number of faces will influence the manner in which the member gains heat. Further information will need to be gathered with respect to determining precisely how simple frames react. A certain amount of knowledge is available; for example, rigid horizontal members will push the top of columns and generate shear forces capable of causing local failure. Rigid uprights will lead to the upward deformation of the horizontal members. In a continuous system, deformation of members some distance from the fire's seat can lead to the occurrence of local hinges or fulcrum points causing cracking and failure.

The next stage is to determine the effect of heat within the section of the member, within the reinforcement steel for example. This can be done by using the available computer programs. The temperature rise within lightweight aggregate concrete is at a lower rate owing to the lower thermal diffusivity of the material. A beam sustaining heat on three faces will have a higher rate of temperature rise than a slab. An I-shaped beam will experience higher temperatures in its central zone compared to a rectangular beam in a similar heat transfer situation, therefore the reinforcement will also reach higher temperatures. The temperature rise in a column is likely to be more rapid than that for a beam of similar width. Data exists giving the temperature isotherms for particular sizes of columns and beams.

The design of flexural concrete members needs to incorporate the following procedures. 1. Calculate the maximum design load for the element. 2. Calculate the maximum applied moment. 3. Calculate the ultimate moment capacity. 4. Determine the average temperature of steel reinforcement. 5. Calculate the reduced tensile force capacity. 6. Ascertain the average temperature of the concrete in the compression zone. 7. Calculate the reduced compressive free capacity. 8. Equate tensile and compressive forces. 9. Calculate the reduced moment resistance and compare this with the already determined maximum applied moment; if this exceeds the maximum applied moment then the design is satisfactory.

Tests on reinforced concrete columns show that they fall into two categories: one where the failure is predominantly in compression and the other where buckling leads to collapse. A column which is seen to be short with respect to slenderness ratio in normal design procedures can behave like a thin column and buckle. This is because when exposed to an open fire the outer layers of concrete attain a higher temperature than the inner zones and consequently the strength of the outer layers reduces at a faster rate. Using computational techniques it has been found that (a) the thermal properties of concrete, (b) the concrete cover to the reinforcement, (c) the amount of reinforcement, and (d) the ratio between the applied load and ultimate load, are the main critical factors in determining fire resistance. On this basis the fire resistance of columns is proportional to their cross-sectional area: the larger the size the better the fire resistance. In the design of concrete frames the joints, sizes and layouts of members should be properly detailed. During construction on site a design should be followed accurately to minimise the effects of fire. Poor workmanship or disregard to the details of design could lead to premature spalling during a fire which will quickly reduce a member's strength.

In high temperatures the point of contraflexure in a span is towards the centre, therefore continuity reinforcements should be extended to prevent the occurrence of flexural shear cracks. It is good practice to have at least 20% of the top reinforcement covering the whole span; where the edge beams provide restraint against rotation, slab reinforcement should be tied in and ends looped or given adequate anchorage length; junctions of slabs and intermediate beams should be given enough reinforcement to provide composite action – but not too much – to prevent ductile failure. The use of stirrups near supports will prevent bond failure, especially with pre-tensioned, pre-stressed units. The bearings for simply supported members should be a minimum of 75mm dimension for one-hour fire resistance and 100mm for above one hour. Columns should be well bonded to beams with reinforced joints in precast as well as *in situ* construction, and the use of links or dowels may be required when composite construction, both precast and *in situ*, is undertaken. It may be found necessary to provide additional protection and this can be achieved by applying a further coating to the concrete; dense cement rendering, gypsum plaster, lightweight gypsum plaster and sprayed mineral fibre are all possible coatings.

COMPARTMENTATION

The basic principle of compartmentation is the fact that the smaller the volume, the less is the fire load. Therefore, by dividing a building into enclosed areas able to resist the spread of fire, the overall safety of the occupants and the structure can be increased. By increasing the degree of compartmentation the fire ratings of the structural elements themselves can be reduced. Compartment walls and floors may be perforated and any communicating doors must have a total fire resistance equal to the fire resistance of the compartment enclosing wall or floor. As previously mentioned, these doors need to comply with the FOC rules. Compartment walls and floors sub-divide a building for the purposes of separating occupancies within that building or giving smaller volumes to restrict the spread of fires. The most essential aspect of compartment walls and floors is that there should be no combustible material passing through the membrane or bypassing its edges to link the areas on either side. Any small openings must be capable of being sealed, and services which perforate the membranes must be fabricated in non-combustible materials. Large service ducts will need linked doors to close in case of fire.

The relationship between (a) the prospective occupiers' space needs, (b) the discreteness of the users, (c) the fire load with respect to building volume, (d) the materials used in the structure, and (e) the initial costs and fire insurance costs, substantially determine the form and overall cost of a building. The use of concrete in floors automatically provides separation between floors. Problems can arise in factories where production processes require uninterrupted floor areas but compartmentation is required for the reduction of risk. The Building Regulations 1985 Approved Document B provides details on compartmentation, on volumes related to purpose groups, on resistance to fire and on the treatment of openings in walls and floors.

VENTILATION AND SMOKE CONTROL

The 1985 Building Regulations for the first time make specific reference to the prevention of the spread of smoke from a fire. In order to mitigate the spread of smoke, which is the major cause of death in fires, a knowledge of its behaviour in buildings is required. The Building Regulations indicate some of its characteristics. Smoke rises and in very high spaces will cool and fail to set off either alarms or high-level sprinklers unless smoke detectors are used. Heat convection sets up air currents in medium and low spaces which can spread the smoke plume and reverse the direction of smoke as it cools and falls. This can disguise the direction of the fire.

Movement should be limited by screens, forming ventilated smoke reservoirs. Smoke will travel horizontally from a fire below a gallery or low area in a large volume before spreading upwards into the main space. Smoke plumes need to be kept compact by the use of screens or baffles so as to avoid damage over large areas and to ensure rapid ventilation via bypass ducts or exhaust systems. The size of smoke reservoirs should be limited so as to minimise the spread of smoke, and its cooling and downward mixing with clear air. To allow smoke to be exhausted at a high level, air must enter at a low level. In spaces such as atriums, high-level corridors are at risk and must be suitably protected. Within large spaces linked by staircases, the staircases should be freestanding or placed in large wells so that smoke can bypass them. Ventilation for smoke can be provided by: (a) permanent, high-level, natural cross-ventilation; (b) natural ventilation through heat-destructible roof-lights; and (c) active measures such as fusible-link-operated roof-vents and air pressure systems.

HIDDEN SPACES

Fire can spread undetected throughout a building by way of enclosed and hidden spaces in the structure. This factor was a major contributor to the loss of life in the Summerland fire described in *Building Technology 3*. The designer and builder should bear the following points in mind when considering the creation of a hidden space. Suspended ceilings should be resistant to the spread of flame. Fire stops in ceiling voids must not be bypassed by combustible materials in the structure of the ceiling at its junction with fire protecting screens or partitions. Ducting or trunking carrying air between protected spaces should be provided with automatic smoke dampers. Those areas separated for reasons of fire safety should have no hidden spaces allowing communication between them. If any spaces do contain services they must be fabricated in non-combustible materials, or sheathed in non-combustible materials, or else the enclosure itself must be fully fire protected. Any access into these spaces must be fire protected, with no access possible from a fire escape stair. Hazardous services running close to each other should be placed in separate spaces.

WORKMANSHIP

The greatest responsibility in providing adequate passive fire resistance measures lies with the designer of the building, but if the detail is not adhered to, or work is carelessly carried out by the builder, the fire resistance properties can be negated. Compliance with the materials' specification, especially with regard to services, is essential. Brickwork and blockwork enclosing protected shafts, etc. should be well-built with no cracks. Concrete floors in vertical ducts should be to full thickness and completely sealed around penetrating services. Any applied fire protection, whether to concrete, timber or steel must be to the specified thickness all over and properly and carefully applied. There should be no passage of air between vertical ducts, or voids created by suspended ceilings. Any hidden spaces or ducts must be thoroughly cleaned out.

SUMMARY

In general terms, the fire safety demands of a building are dependent upon four factors, namely *purpose*, *size*, *separation* (or division) and *resistance to fire*. These factors are considered in assessing risk to the building in place. The largest problem is in the exposure hazard, with respect to radiant heat causing fire to spread across intervening spaces from one building to another or from part to part of the same building. This risk factor governs two aspects of design: first, the distance between a building and its site boundary or an adjoining building, and, second, the manner in which the volume of the building is arranged. The possible fire hazard of a building is based on its fire load, which is determined by its use and size.

The relationship between buildings, boundary and adjoining buildings is important, and where buildings are separated they, perhaps paradoxically, give greater cause for concern than if they were connected, as in a terraced row of houses. Each house is considered to be a separate compartment, with the separating or party walls providing adequate fire resistance. Separate buildings have necessary spaces between them and it is these spaces, described as 'undefended' spaces, which can create problems. The walls, and openings in them, overlooking these spaces can expose the area of fire risk. Narrow spaces can behave like flues; a contained, smoke-logged space exposed to a sudden ingress of oxygen and heat might provide the conditions for an explosion. Walls burning or collapsing can reduce fire safety for the building's occupants, and opposite openings can create fire routes.

The Building Regulations 1985 Approved Document B, *Fire Spread*, provides techniques for ascertaining the allowable perforations in external walls and roofs with respect to their normal fire resistance and the proximity of the site boundary or other buildings. The fire resistance of the envelope's materials needs to be considered with respect to the building's fire resistance as a whole and the hazard of spread to other buildings.

A further consideration with respect to the siting of a building is its ease of access, for both ingress and egress, but with particular reference to accessibility for fire fighting appliances and personnel. A fire path will need to be provided for wheeled fire fighting appliances. Details such as path widths, turning circles, maximum gradients, space requirements for ladders, and the provision of hydrants and wet and dry rising mains within the building, will need to be agreed with the local fire brigade.

QUESTIONS

1. Describe the relationship between the fire load, the use and the size of a building, giving examples drawn from different purpose groups.
2. Discuss how steel performs in fire, and the means by which it can be protected. How does it compare with concrete?
3. Draw up a quality control checklist for ensuring compliance with passive fire resistance requirements during the process of construction.

12. Active Fire Precautions

Active fire precautions must be seen as an integral part of the measures adopted to reduce or contain the effects of fire in buildings. Items and systems once seen as expensive bonuses to fire safety are now considered as economic and life-preserving essentials. Active precautions can be considered under five main headings: *detectors and alarms, first-aid fire extinguishing equipment, facilities to assist the fire service*, the installation of *automatic fire extinguishing equipment*, and *fire and explosion suppressants*. Each of these is now considered in turn.

DETECTORS AND ALARMS

A number of criteria determine the choice of detectors and alarms. These can be summarised as:

(a) *The value of automatic detection*, based on fires occurring in the early morning or at the end of the working day, where there is a tendency for delay in the calling of the fire brigade, and where fire occurs in parts of a building which are unoccupied at night or infrequently visited.

(b) *The speed of detection*, related to the response time of the fire brigade or the internal active fire extinguishing systems. Within a building the rapidity of detection is affected by height of ceiling, profile of a ceiling; shape of room or corridor at fire source; insulation characteristics of roof or ceiling; horizontal distance of fire from detector; loss of products of combustion up stairwells, etc; and the presence of ventilation current or air inlets.

Detectors come in three main types: *heat detectors, smoke detectors* and *flame detectors*. The choice of detector can vary according to circumstances; for example, heat detectors are used in confined spaces or where cooking (producing some smoke) is carried out. Smoke detectors can be sited at the highest point in a space and can give advance warning of fire before flame ignition occurs. Flame detectors are best used outdoors, by, for example, chemical stores and manufacturers. In any one building all three types may be installed to meet the conditions in particular areas.

Alongside the detectors there should be some form of alarm,

and this in turn should be related to a particular area of the building so as to locate the position of the fire hazard. Alarms are usually auditory, with perhaps an intermittent warning tone followed by a continuous tone demanding immediate evacuation. The detectors and alarms can be linked to sprinkler systems which immediately come into operation on fire detection. The alarm can also be communicated directly and automatically to the local fire station to initiate call-out. A comprehensive detection and alarm system can be installed which will provide security cover, too, in addition to fire cover. Any automatic detection and alarm system should be possible to operate manually. It may also be necessary to install visual alarms, especially in places where ear-muffs are required.

FIRST-AID FIRE EXTINGUISHING EQUIPMENT

Such equipment consists primarily of hand-held fire extinguishers (with various contents) and small hose reels permanently connected to a water supply. In some areas such as kitchens, fire blankets should be provided. Problems may arise in providing highly visible places to store this first-aid equipment, as well as in its subsequent maintenance to a state of readiness. These items should be adjacent to escape doors or to areas of special hazards, such as stores of inflammable materials or risky work stations. They should also be placed in staircase and entry lobbies leading to primary circulation routes. It is best to group items of fire fighting equipment together to form easily identifiable stations, consisting of, say, an emergency telephone, a fire alarm, first aid supplies, stretchers, protective clothing, breathing apparatus and portable escape apparatus such as ladders.

FACILITIES TO ASSIST THE FIRE SERVICE

The most important of these facilities is the provision of wet and dry risers, located to bring a supply of water close to the seat of any fire so that it can be fought from inside the building. The wet riser has a fully charged water supply with a hose reel permanently connected to it. The water supply should be independent of the main supply to the building, and of course, at a sufficient pressure. Code of Practice BS 5306 Part 1: 1976 gives recommendations for hose reel installations. Dry risers are placed in buildings so that they provide a fixed pipe for the transference of water from a mobile source into the building, with couplings and valves at each floor level. From the dry riser a potentially unlimited length of hose can be taken to the seat of the fire.

If lifts are installed in the building each car should have control systems which can be operated by experienced fire fighters. On the sounding of a fire alarm the lifts should automatically return to the exit level and remain there under control of a fireman. The operating switch should give absolute control to the person inside the lift, cancelling any prior instructions, and when stopping at the floor its doors should remain open until operated again internally. The provision of a telephone in the lift is also very useful.

High-risk buildings such as hospitals or very tall multi-storey structures will have emergency power systems. These should cut in automatically on detection of a fire, and operate such items as the lifts and emergency lighting. A manual over-ride should also be provided. Emergency lighting standards are described in the British Standards Code of Practice BS 5266, *Emergency Lighting of Premises*. The lights, (called 'luminaires' in this case) should be sited so that each one is visible from another and capable of being seen in smoky conditions.

AUTOMATIC FIRE EXTINGUISHING EQUIPMENT

Within this category are included the various types of sprinklers, doors and shutters, and forms of smoke control.

The type of sprinkler system used will be based on two criteria: first, the properties of the contents being protected and the possibility that they might be damaged by accidental operation of the sprinkler system, and, second, the fire load hazard of the contents and the rate and type of discharge required to make the fire area safe. In selecting a sprinkler system it is important to consider the following: (a) the adequacy of the water supply; (b) whether emergency power sources will be required; (c) the choice of system related to different parts and uses of the buildings; (d) the actual position of the sprinkler heads; (e) the necessity of keeping sprinklers with water away from electrical installations; (f) the provision of several layers of sprinklers in high areas; (g) the means of draining the outflow from the sprinklers; (h) the means of draining the system and testing it; (i) the integration of the main supply pipes with the other services in ducts, etc; (j) the provision of flexible runs to accommodate structural or thermal movement; and (k) the ease of checking and maintaining the system.

Doors and shutters may need to be kept open during normal activities, but will need to be closed in the event of fire in order to contain its spread. These doors can be closed by one of two methods: (a) by a fusible link responding to local heat, or (b) by a solenoid switch activated by a local detector. Manual operation should also be possible. The FOC's rules specify details for doors and shutters.

The rapid accumulation of smoke can inhibit the operation of sprinklers (and vice versa) and this is accentuated when using mechanical means to draw out smoke. There are three main mechanically assisted smoke control systems: (a) mechanically opened natural vents, (b) smoke-extracting fans, and (c) ducting external systems. Pressurisation systems in buildings have been experimented with, and their use, although somewhat limited, is documented in Code of Practice BS 5588: Part 4, 1978. Specialist designers are required for its optimal inclusion into buildings.

FIRE AND EXPLOSION SUPPRESSANTS

Normal water sprinkler systems are inappropriate for the control of some types of fires and explosions. Systems using foams, powders and gases can be utilised where special-risk fires might occur.

To summarise, this brief description of active fire precautions has only indicated the main types of systems used. It is expected that detailed knowledge of the systems can be gained elsewhere from the relevant FOC rules and the Codes of Practice, and from standard texts. In general terms the fire safety of a building must be seen as a combination of passive fire protection measures and active precautions which together provide a structure which initially stands up well to a fire and provides adequate means with which to contain or extinguish a fire. An important aspect of fire protection is the provision of means of escape for the building's occupants. This can incorporate elements of both passive and active measures, and is discussed in the next chapter.

QUESTIONS

1. Investigate the types of sprinkler systems available and discuss in what situations they would be most appropriate.
2. Describe the particular problems in providing active fire precautions in a hotel.
3. Explore the ethical issues raised if doors automatically shut but can be opened manually during a fire, thereby initially trapping people.

13. Means of Escape

It is most important when confronted with fire to ensure the safety of people. Primarily this means affording them a safe route out of the building. The building itself, via its passive fire protection measures, should withstand the effects of fire for a period of time before partial or complete collapse. This should allow time for the escape of the occupants and for fire fighting to commence in order to prevent the spread of the fire, and eventually extinguish it. Active fire precautions can aid the safe exit of people from the building through the provision of illuminated exit signs and sprinklers over and adjacent to exit doors. The basic design of the building – doors, staircases, and distances between doors and places of occupation – will determine the ease with which people can escape in case of a fire. Early in the design stage the architect must incorporate the basic escape route requirements into the form of the building. In later stages the question of specifying the right materials for walls, floors, doors and staircases will need to be addressed.

A point to note at the outset of this discussion on means of escape is the manner in which the UK Building Regulations treat the matter. The basic philosophy behind the regulations is that there is a statutory set of rules, with clauses determining health and hygiene (including, here, drainage). These are couched in general performance terms: 'reasonable' and 'satisfactory' specifying the standards to be achieved. In some instances the regulations are more prescriptive, however. Accompanying the statutory clauses are a series of Approved Documents and Schedules. In all cases bar one these give details of current knowledge and practical experience which can be used by designers and builders to meet the statutory requirements. It is open to technologists to put forward their own solutions to meet the requirements which do not concur with the methods stated in the Approved Documents. If these alternatives can be seen to be practical and meet the performance requirements (by, for example, being awarded an Agrément Certificate) then the approving authorities will allow them to be used. It is hoped that this will allow technologists to research and develop means of achieving a better quality of building construction. In nearly all cases the Documents relate to the relevant British Standards, but as these are *minimum* standards there is scope for both improvement and development.

Approved Document B, *Fire Spread*, has already been mentioned, providing the means of meeting the statutory clauses relating to the prevention of fire spread and maintaining the integrity of the building for notional periods. If the technologist can produce materials or construction details which can be seen to meet the performance requirements then these, although not specifically referred to in the Approved Document, can be used in buildings. The exception to the philosophy of the current regulations is means of escape. In this case, where means of escape measures are required to be applied to a building, then a mandatory document must be consulted. This document categorises buildings into the range of purpose groups and then refers the designer to relevant Codes of Practice and British Standards as the only legal methods by which to achieve performance requirements. The mandatory document does not cover all purpose groups; a notable exception is the case of tall multi-storey structures in high density building areas such as city centres. When the Building Regulations are amended it is expected that all types of buildings in all parts of the UK will be covered.

The problem of providing means of escape can be considered under three main headings: *occupancy characteristics*; *design and planning of escape*; and *construction in relation to means of escape*.

OCCUPANCY CHARACTERISTICS

While it has been recognised for many years that buildings can be categorised into discrete purpose groups, such as *domestic – low-rise, domestic – high-rise, factories, offices* or *assembly halls*, with general characteristics of occupation, it is not until recent years that the behaviour of people in buildings has been investigated, researched and analysed. The results of these investigations are slowly being absorbed into practice, but it is not until a major fire catastrophe occurs that significant measures are adopted. For example, while hotels were seen to be buildings of relative high risk because of usage patterns resulting in higher fire incidence, their fire safety measures were little more sophisticated than those of run-of-the-mill office buildings. The problems of multi-occupancy buildings such as hostels and houses with bed-sit accommodation were not fully perceived until loss of life in fires highlighted the inadequacies of means of escape measures.

There are two aspects of occupancy characteristics to consider beyond the basic distinction according to use or purpose. These are (a) the behaviour of people in the course of normal occupancy activities, and (b) their behaviour in the event of fire. With regard to the former, the occupants' behaviour can dramatically alter the level of fire safety in buildings, resulting in, for example, the non-maintenance of fire extinguishers or emergency lighting equipment, the propping open of fire doors, and, perhaps with worse consequences, the locking of fire escape doors for so-called 'reasons of security'. With regard to the latter, a major factor in how people will react to fire is the degree of familiarity they have with the building. Hotels were mentioned earlier, and it is in this context that a hotel can be seen as having additional risks in the event of fire. People staying in a hotel will be there on a short-term basis and will not be familiar with the building. Even after a relatively lengthy stay their knowledge of the whole building is likely to be scant. In a situation of emotional unrest or near-panic all sense of orientation can be lost. Additionally, even if rationality is still being exercised, the problems of smoke movement in corridors (particularly common in hotels) can give a false indication of the direction of the seat of the fire, and people following an undercurrent of smoke expecting it to lead to a ventilation exit.

The combination of poor maintenance of the fire safety equipment and lack of familiarity with the building can have disastrous consequences in the event of fire. What can the building technologist do to reduce these hazards? Obviously, he will meet the practice and statutory requirements, but as these are usually based on past experience they may not be entirely appropriate for modern buildings and current usage patterns and activities. In the wake of the fire at the Bradford City football ground in 1985 the safety of people in public stadia was investigated. As a consequence a whole range of precautionary measures was instituted, ensuring, for example, the clearance of litter which could provide fuel for a fire, and the means of escape for people in covered stands. At the root of the problem is the behaviour of people and how they react, or fail to react, to the threat of fire. The 'it'll never happen to me' attitude is common – and understandable, as the consequences of 'it' happening are horrific and will be put to one side in the course of everyday living. Bearing this in mind, it is the responsibility of technologists and building owners or managers to plan and act on all available knowledge and advice to mitigate the risks. For example, if the Bradford City Football Club had heeded the warning from its local fire officer regarding the fire risk of the accumulation of rubbish beneath the stands, and had cleared it, then the fire spread might not have been so rapid nor the loss of life so great.

In this connection, a proposal for making building owners or occupiers take legal responsibility for the maintenance of fire safety measures has been advocated in a government report (*Review of the Fire Precautions Act 1971*, Home Office, 1985). The fulfilment of these obligations would be monitored by the local fire authority, with the power to enforce compliance, making the owner or occupier liable to legal proceedings if requirements were not met.

The technologist should be aware of current knowledge with respect to the behaviour of people in fire and should at all times during design (and also construction) consult with fire officers and with experts in fire technology. On completion and hand-over of the building, the relevant fire precautions should be explained to the client or user, along with the ways and means to maintain the highest levels of fire safety. For example, the technologist should use the best type of locks and furniture on exit doors to meet the demands of security and ease of exit. In theory, cost should not be a prime consideration where human life is at risk, but in practice value for money should be sought in the specification. The client should be informed of the reasons for such costs, and provided with a documented explanation of the rationale, measures and route of the means of escape, stressing the importance of effective maintenance.

DESIGN AND PLANNING OF ESCAPE ROUTES

In the planning of escape routes a number of factors need to be considered, illustrated in Fig. 3.3. Each factor is now explained and discussed:

(a) *Escape time*. The time needed for escape is dependent upon the rate of growth of the fire, the point at which the occupants become aware of its existence and the time at which conditions become critical for the occupants. Therefore, the escape time

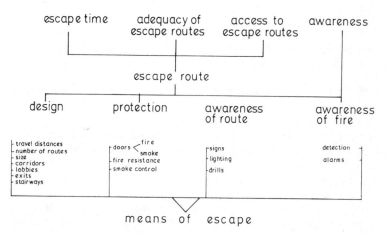

Fig. 3.3 *Factors affecting means of escape*

is determined by occupant characteristics, the rate of travel possible, and the ambient conditions. As previously mentioned, familiarity with the building will have the greatest effect on rate of travel and subsequent escape time. This is termed the *human factor*. Escape time cannot be considered independently of other factors influenced by the building's design. Time and building layout factors are interrelated with the factor of the number of people escaping.

(b) *Adequacy of escape route*. Important here are the widths of corridors, the integrity of the structures and bottle-necks in the flow of people. The main factor governing adequacy is the width of the routes, but too wide a corridor can cause disorientation if the walls cannot be seen in smoky conditions.

(c) *Access to escape route*. At all times, free unobstructed access should be provided to escape routes. People will need to move from an unprotected area to a protected area (the escape route) both easily and quickly.

(d) *Awareness*. The first warning of fire is usually given by word of mouth. Initially, an alarm or detection device (if installed) will give notification but after that word spreads throughout the building, even though an alarm may sound.

Under the heading *design* in Fig. 3.3 are a number of specific factors which must be assessed. The distance from unprotected to protected zone needs to be minimised (the Codes of Practice give maximum distances). Also, the length of the escape route should be minimised, with the aim of allowing people to escape from the building to a safe place in the shortest distance. If the distance from unprotected zone to protected zone is excessive, or if the building contains large numbers of people, a number of escape routes will need to be provided. Their size (in particular, width) will be dependent on the number of people expected to use them. In most situations in large buildings the route moves from place of occupation to an area of local circulation; from then on the route must be a protected zone, consisting of a fire resisting corridor leading to a ventilated lobby or protected staircase, and then to either an internal collection area or to outside the building via the final exit.

In providing the protected zone the notional fire resistance is related to the purpose group of the building, within which the walls and floors of the route need to meet specific requirements. Doors must be able to withstand fire, and prevent smoke from entering the route. The lobbies and staircases need to have means of ventilation to disperse any smoke that might enter.

It has already been stated that awareness of the route, the human factor, is at the core of effective escape, so the designer must make routes simple and well defined, and aid the escape by marking them with clear signs. Emergency lighting along the route and for the signs should be provided. In the case of buildings with large numbers of people in day-long occupation, fire drills need to be undertaken. Even if the building's occupants are transient, as in the case of a leisure centre, drills need to be carried out so that the building's managers and employees have some experience in the event of emergency.

When all the above factors have been assessed and integrated into the plan of the building, the designer should attempt to visualise the behaviour of people in the event of fire and simulate their escape from the building. There is a strong interaction between the main factors and the components for escape route design. Figure 3.4 demonstrates these relationships. The designer will need to draw on a number of specialists in order to create an escape route which is of optimum value. Smoke control needs to be confidently determined; research into the human factor needs to be consulted; and the fire authority must be involved during all stages of the design process.

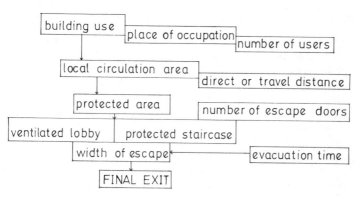

Fig. 3.4   *Escape route design*

CONSTRUCTION IN RELATION TO MEANS OF ESCAPE

The integrity of the escape route must be maintained by using materials and construction of predictable behaviour, which are either fire resistant or have low flame spread characteristics. The route must be enclosed but also allow access and egress. Therefore, doors must be fire resistant and openings must deny the passage of smoke. The control of smoke is a major factor in the construction of escape routes. Initially, smoke should be prevented from entering the escape route but if it does (when people use the doors) it should be evacuated.

The fire resistance of the walls and floors of the route must meet the notional requirements. Staircases must be fire resistant, and in multi-occupancy buildings they must be enclosed, so as to provide a safe escape route. Where lobbies are required the doors and walls must meet the prevailing fire resistance standards.

In all situations the standards of workmanship should be of the highest level. An ill-fitting door can allow smoke or flame to penetrate into the escape route, causing delays in escape and possibly allowing a fire to spread.

This chapter, on means of escape, points to its high level of importance in fire technology. The first consideration in the event of fire must be *the saving of human life*, following by *the prevention of damage to the property* and *the prevention of fire spread*. The prime objective of escape routes is to ensure the safe evacuation of all occupants of a building in the event of fire to a place of safety. Escape routes should be available from all parts of the building; they should remain safe and effective for the time during which they may be needed; they should be clearly visible to all users and be located and sized to meet the needs of all occupants according to the use of the building. The basic stages of designing an optimum escape route can be summarised as follows:

1. determine occupancy loading, human factors and escape times
2. determine the need and desirability for a detection system
3. plan layout with unprotected and protected zones based on travel distances to give suitable escape times
4. determine means of smoke control
5. ensure floor exits and escape staircases are as far apart as possible
6. calculate the flow rates of people in corridors, exits and stairs to determine their minimum width
7. determine the need for smoke lobbies
8. evaluate the need for and position of signs, lighting, etc.

The previous chapters have outlined the fundamentals of fire technology as related to the building and its use. Knowledge of fire technology is growing, and, consequently, the design and construction sectors are developing means of dealing with the possibility of fire. The following two chapters will examine current developments in fire technology.

QUESTIONS

1. Investigate the physiological effects of a fire upon those involved.
2. Means of escape in case of fire have been defined as 'Structural means forming an integral part of a building whereby people

can escape from fire by their own unaided efforts to a place of safety'. Discuss the meaning of this definition.
3. Outline the main points you would raise in commenting upon a building's design with respect to means of escape.

14. Fire Safety Engineering

In order to make sense of the substantial body of knowledge and practice relating to the fire safety of buildings it is customary to consider the measures identified in the previous chapter under the headings of *passive fire protection*, *active fire precautions* and *means of escape*.

Where fire is considered in relation to buildings it is presented piecemeal in the statute books. The Building Regulations 1985 give guidance and details, mainly with reference to relevant British Standards and Codes of Practice. The now defunct London Building Acts, with their clauses and procedures, may also be consulted. Another important statute is The Fire Precautions Act 1971. Together these documents cover most aspects of fire safety, but there are still gaps in the provision of guidance for good practice. Additionally there is now a body of research on the behaviour of materials and the effects of fire and the products of combustion. This allows some confident predictions of performance to be made. In the making of predictions, measurable and quantifiable criteria need to be adopted. In the past much assessment of risk to a building has been based on experience and best judgements; it has taken the form, in other words, of a subjective evaluation.

Much of the available knowledge of fire in buildings is spread around a number of publications, considered piecemeal in studies which do not fully take into account recent research and experience. One way in which a more accurate and clearer assessment of fire safety can be made is to undertake some form of rational and quantifiable approach to assessing fire hazard, making an evaluation of fire safety measures in their entirety. This approach can be identified as *fire safety engineering*, as promulgated by H.L. Malhotra (*Fire Safety in Buildings*, a Building Research Establishment Report, published by the Department of the Environment, HMSO, 1986). The aim of any system is to balance fire safety measures with the fire hazard assessment by determining the best economic combination of alternatives.

There have been several attempts to produce methods or systems which provide a substantial basis for balancing hazard against fire safety measures. One example is a scheme for assessing the fire safety needs of health care buildings in Edinburgh. This was produced by the Department of Fire Safety

Engineering and presented by E.W. Marchant in a paper entitled 'A cost effective approach to fire safety: the Points System' at the IFSSEC (International Fire Safety and Service Engineers Committee) Conference in London, in April 1984. Twenty key safety factors were identified and given values, when noted in practice, from 0 to 5 (5 being the most perfect). Each of the factors was then multiplied by a contribution factor based on another scheme known as the Delphi System. In this, risk factors such as patient mobility are given a value, ranging from 1.0 to 4.5. Other risk factors include patient density, fire zone location, average age and patient/attendant ratio. The other part of the equation consists of safety parameters: values are given to such items as construction type, doors in corridors, smoke control, internal finishes and sprinklers. Some of these safety parameters can be awarded a negative value as an indication of the increase in hazard which can result from sub-standard construction in existing buildings. In the final analysis it is expected that Total Risk = ‹ Safety Level. In the Edinburgh scheme a total value sum was calculated to give an overall safety level. Where the total exceeded 450 points the safety was considered *good*; 350 to 450 was *acceptable*; 280 to 350 *not readily acceptable*; and less than 280 *completely unacceptable*.

Another approach, developed in the USA, uses logic and decision trees. The use of these has already been discussed (see pp.119–21). These have now been augmented by a further approach: *analytical modelling*. In its simplest form this modelling produces fire scenarios based on the mathematical relationships necessary for a set of conditions to exist. So far, models of fire growth, smoke behaviour and toxic hazards have been developed. The use of these models can assist the study of the qualitative and quantitative effects that constructional or other features have on fire growth and spread. Computer-based models have been developed to simulate the effect of fire on structures, by considering the heat flow into a section and its consequent effect on the load-bearing capabilities of the elements. These programs are becoming more realistic with the integration of material behaviour models. Further models demonstrate the movements of people in corridors and on stairways. In all cases the analytical and computer-based models are an improvement on the test procedures, which have, erroneously, been considered beyond criticism in the past. Analytical procedures have been seen to be more consistent than tests. Eventually, quantitative techniques will begin to achieve high levels of predictability in relation to the behaviour of fire in given circumstances, where construction layout, furnishing and occupancy are known. The fire safety measures finally adopted by a designer will be based on social, political and economic factors. Such factors have already been presented in the conceptual framework of this series, in *Building*

Technology 1 and, in greater detail, in *Building Technology 3*. Some aspects of these wider issues will be discussed in the next chapter.

At present there is some scope for the adoption of these quantitative methods. In the USA and Canada limited permission has been given to use them for the planning of means of escape. Within the 1985 Building Regulations in the UK there is scope to allow designers to use alternative approaches to those suggested. As long as designers demonstrate that reliable techniques have been employed in obtaining solutions they should be able to meet the requirements of the approving authorities.

A spin-off from the development of fire safety engineering is the growth of a discrete body of knowledge with its own entourage of experts. The disparate approach to fire problems has already been mentioned, and its status as a recognisable discipline has not developed as much as it might. Indeed, the absorption of the Fire Research Station into the Building Research Establishment could be seen as a lessening of the importance of research into fire. There is no longer an identifiable centre of excellence promoting research into fires in buildings. Architects, designers, builders and surveyors have comparatively little knowledge of fire technology, and only really begin to understand it when they tackle it in the design and construction of buildings with supposedly high fire risks, such as shopping malls, high-rise offices and public buildings. Yet statistics show that the highest number of fatalities and injuries occur in fires in dwellings, and are mainly caused by the inhalation of fire gases (*Fire statistics*, HMSO 1983).

In real terms, property losses through fire have remained virtually steady for a number of years. As the majority of building professionals are concerned with designing, constructing, altering and maintaining dwellings of one type or another it is essential that their attention should be drawn to a better appreciation of the problem of fire. Although builders and designers are aware of fire hazards, and understand the need for fire resistant structures and escape routes, too few critically consider a design in relation to the possibility of fire, or give specific advice to clients on fire safety in the dwelling. The use of some double glazing systems can hinder the escape of people from the upper stories of a house or flat if the stairs are unusable. The increased use of insulation for thermal conservation can increase the effects of fire, promoting a faster rise in temperature. Defects and carelessness in workmanship can allow the spread of fire to be excessive. Certain methods of construction can be perceived to have a higher fire risk. Some concern has been expressed in the UK regarding the greater risk of timber framed houses in the case of fire, although if properly protected according to standard practice these structures have no greater risk than traditional masonry.

As fire safety engineering develops it is hoped that it will bring in its wake a wider awareness of the problems – and the solutions which can be adopted by building professionals. The future could see the advent of fire safety engineers, acting independently or within design and design/build organisations, giving advice on the proper measures required to increase the safety of people in all buildings in the event of fire.

QUESTIONS

1. Discuss the viability of using computer programs for assessing the behaviour of fire in proposed designs.
2. Comment on the proposal to introduce fire safety engineers.
3. Discuss the possibility of drawing together all fire safety legislation under one unifying act. Detail both the advantages and the disadvantages.

15. Fire Technology

In this final chapter on fire technology the relationships between its constituent elements will be analysed, and some observations and comments made on present and future developments. The elements of fire technology can be identified as: (a) fire hazard; (b) fire resistance; (c) escape of people from fire; (d) fire safety management; (e) fire safety engineering; (f) legislation; (g) social attitudes and values; (h) functional requirements; (i) technological change and development; and (j) economics. The safety factor is the paramount consideration, which provides the rationale for fire technology.

THREE ELEMENTS OF FIRE SAFETY

First, a reminder of three of the constituent elements: *fire hazard* is the risk of a fire occurring in a building, and is related to the occupants' use activities; the *fire resistance* of a building is designed to maintain its structural integrity and to prevent the spread of fire, via passive or active measures within and without the envelope; the *escape of people* to a place of safety is a prime aim of fire safety and the various passive measures make a major contribution to achieving this. In combining these three elements a building can be seen to afford the required standards of fire safety. Our first discussion point is centred on the combination of these three aspects.

Under present practice and legislation the three factors above are not fully integrated within a total system. Within their own parameters they provide effective measures, and experience has produced efficient design and constructions. Each can be said to meet the required criteria in its own right. With respect to each, research and development has, and still is, providing knowledge on fire behaviour, the behaviour of materials in fire and the behaviour of people in fire. Links between these aspects of research are being made: for example, the behaviour of people in escape corridors may be affected by the behaviour of concrete beams in fire. It is now possible to forecast, qualitatively and quantitatively, standards of fire safety based on sound data and numerical analysis. The deployment and use of technologically sophisticated equipment such as smoke detectors and fast-response sprinkler systems can tip the balance in fire safety.

Traditionally, the emphasis has been on ensuring that the structure of a building is unaffected by fire for a notional period of time so that people can escape efficiently. The structure's integrity provides time for the fire brigade to arrive and fight the fire. The building itself does not actively respond to the presence of fire. Some recognition is now being given to the possibility of balancing, or producing trade-offs, between the three fire safety elements, particularly with respect to the design of fire resistant buildings. The UK Building Regulations 1985 now allow a doubling of compartment size in shops if a sprinkler system is used. There is some evidence to suggest that an increase in compartment size does not proportionally increase fire severity. Recent research has shown that a doubling of the floor area of a compartment, with a comparable increase in openings in its external walls, results in an increase in fire severity of about 12% – far less than previous assumptions. In the future it may be possible to have larger compartment sizes (related to use), carefully designed to vent adequately any fire, and to control initially its propagation by the use of devices such as sprinklers. A trade-off could be made between passive and active measures. Malhotra has recommended that compartment sizes can be selected according to building *type*, whether single-storey, high-rise or basement, and whether equipped with a sprinkler installation or not. If the prime concern is with life safety some maximum areas need to be set, based on the minimum fire resistance. Compartment area should be considered in the contexts of its situation and active precautionary measures.

Published fire statistics (*Fire Statistics*, HMSO, 1984) cite the estimate made by the fire brigade of the interval between ignition and the discovery of a fire. From this information it can be conjectured that an earlier discovery of fire could reduce fatal, as well as non-fatal, injuries. There is a higher casualty rate for fires discovered more than five minutes after ignition. The early detection of a fire has a significant effect on life safety, and it can also have some effect on property protection so long as early detection leads to early measures to control the fire. This will now be considered with respect to safety in dwellings.

The previous chapter mentioned the fact that the majority of casualties in fires occur in domestic situations. An investigation carried out in the USA (*Fire in the United States*, Fourth Edition, Federal Emergency Management Agency, Washington DC, 1981) indicated that a possible 50% reduction in fatalities could be achieved by using single-station smoke detectors. Unfortunately, in practice this has not reduced fatalities. This could be due to either inadequate maintenance or to non-recognition of the problem.

Should smoke detectors, therefore, be recommended for domestic buildings? Fire brigades and insurance companies recommend the installation of smoke detectors, and insurance premium rates may become linked to the active fire safety measures utilised in dwellings, as they are now in commercial and public buildings. Currently, there is considerable publicity regarding simple fire precaution equipment available for domestic use. Smoke detectors are available off-the-shelf in most do-it-yourself stores in the UK, and it is likely that their sales figures will reach those of intruder alarm systems. Most detectors are installed by the occupier, but perhaps the building technologist ought to see these as an integral part of the specification for new dwellings.

Smoke detectors can be found in new, highly-priced individual houses, where they are seen as a protection measure against damage to a large property investment. With the growth of domestic property ownership in the UK there will be a concurrent concern with protection. In other words, it is likely that the use of such devices as smoke detectors will be encouraged by fiscal considerations rather than by concern for life. Insurance companies might offer lower premiums which, together with an emphasis on investment and future resale values, will promote the use of active fire precautions. As these are installed in existing dwellings social expectation will demand their installation in *new* dwellings. Therefore, designers and builders will need to learn to specify such precautions. Their cost is quite low – at 1987 prices a pair of smoke detectors costs less than £50. However, as research in the USA indicates, smoke detectors do not appear to have brought about any reduction in the number of fire casualties. This must be considered in relation to the manner in which fire safety measures are maintained and managed – in the case of multi-occupancy buildings. This is the next point for discussion.

FIRE SAFETY MANAGEMENT

The aim of fire safety management is two-fold. First, to ensure that the fire safety measures which have been provided are kept in good order, and, second, to initiate actions which will help and assist the occupants to reach a place of safety. In a number of recent major fires in public buildings the response of the managers of the buildings has been unsatisfactory; there was no preparation for a case of emergency. Additionally, in some cases there were instances where the means of escape were obstructed. For example, padlocks and chains were put on escape doors, with no keys available. Any provisions relating to fire are primarily directed at new buildings or refurbishments, coming under the control of the Building Regulations. Some categories of existing buildings still need to comply with fire safety measures such as the Fire Precautions Act 1971; these need to be inspected and must obtain the relevant certificate. Once this has been given there is no follow-up mechanism to ensure continuing compliance. The building's users are left to their own habits of occupation. Fire doors may be propped open; detector systems may not be tested; means of escape can become obstructed by furniture; the occupiers may not have been directly informed of the procedures in the case of fire, let alone carried out a practice drill.

Malhotra has identified the three vital components of any fire safety plan, and these are shown in Fig. 3.5. A maintenance plan ought to be the responsibility of the person who implements work on the structure, fabric or services of a building. This can be seen as a direct off-shoot from building technology as it involves a knowledge of construction. It shows the importance of giving full consideration to the interrelationship between design, production and maintenance (as analysed in *Building Technology 3*). By ensuring that the technical solutions adopted during the design and production stages are considered in relation to the users' habits of occupation the need for maintenance of the fire safety system should be minimised. For example, a fire door which is known to be subject to heavy and constant use (leaving it vulnerable to being propped open) will need a strong, heavy-duty door-closer, with perhaps some further measures to ensure that it is allowed to close, such as a sign or audible alarm which announces that it has been left open. Detectors usually require power sources, although some can operate from batteries. The integrity of power supplies to these should be checked. A major criticism levelled against the use of sprinklers is their poor reliability. Proper procedures need to be implemented to ensure that water supplies are always maintained and that activating mechanisms are functioning.

The layout and provision of escape routes ought to be known to all occupants of the building. This will not be possible if these are casual users, as in the case of a leisure centre – in which a greater responsibility lies with the managing employees to be fully conversant with escape routes. To aid them, and the other users of the building, clear information in the form of signs needs to be displayed to give guidance in the event of fire. Rubbish anywhere is a fire hazard and should be quickly cleared. The type and position of heat sources should be carefully monitored. In the UK it is common to use free-standing paraffin and cylinder gas heaters. These are a constant source of fires.

In buildings such as hotels, leisure centres, shops and multi-storey offices, where there are large numbers of people who may be unfamiliar with the building, there needs to be a positive approach to apportioning responsibility. Staff ought to be appointed to carry out certain duties, for example ensuring that all

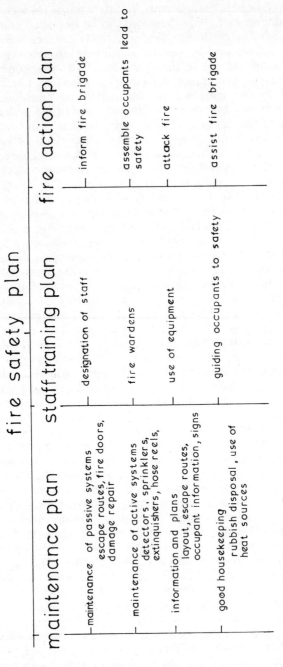

Fig. 3.5 *Plan for fire safety*

fire doors are working effectively. In large buildings with active fire fighting equipment some people ought to be trained in its use. In the case of a building open to the public, some staff should be responsible for guiding the public to a place of safety in the event of a fire. This information should be imparted to *all* staff so that they are aware of who is responsible for what.

A fully described and, ideally, practised procedure should be implemented to deal initially with a fire. Whether or not automatic systems have been installed they should be capable of being operated manually so that people are able to override any automatic device. Assistance to the fire brigade should be concentrated on the provision of information and guidance rather than help in continuing to fight the fire after the initial first-aid activities.

Much of what has been advocated above necessarily takes place after hand-over of a building to a client, and for practical purposes is not the responsibility of the building technologist. Nevertheless, there is a part to be played by the conscientious and caring professional. Approximately half of the total volume of building work is in refurbishment, alteration, repair and maintenance to existing buildings. Here the technologist can be in direct contact with a building's owners or occupiers. In these circumstances it will be possible to advise people on all aspects of safety in fire. As it is expected that the technologist will be aware of current practice and initiatives, he will be doing the client a disservice if he does not put forward suggestions regarding the optimum use of fire safety measures. This should range from considering the trade-offs between active and passive measures to giving detailed proposals for the effective management of the system when the building is in use. The Fire Protection Association and an appendix to BS 5588 can give basic guidance in the development of working documents that will apply fire safety management principles to a particular building and its occupiers. A change of use in a building can completely change its fire safety requirements, even though passive and active measures may remain the same. Therefore, a new fire safety plan will need to be devised.

FIRE SAFETY ENGINEERING

The concept of fire safety engineering has already been discussed in Chapter 7 so only a few general points will be made here. First, it must be seen as a constituent strand in the discipline of fire technology, and one which is based on developing a body of knowledge on a scientific basis. If, as is likely, further research will be carried out relating to all aspects of fire in buildings, this may itself be seen as embracing all aspects of fire technology. Experts may be able to give direct inputs into the design and construction processes, advising building technologists, owners and occupiers, and influencing the views of society as a whole and of the government. In other words, the fire safety engineer will be a *fire technologist*. This will have particular implications for building technology. Will it be necessary then to impart knowledge on fire safety to students of building technology? It is perhaps likely that a separate discipline dedicated to fire problems will be able to provide all the necessary expertise. Will fire technology develop from the work of architects, general builders and service engineers, or from scientific research? What links should there be between fire equipment manufacturers, professional building institutions, government research bodies and commercial enterprises? Should approval and control be vested in fire brigades, local authority building inspectorates or independent approved organisations? What say should fire insurance companies have on measures and policies? Could they provide a home for fire safety engineers, or would this conflict too greatly with the business objective of making a profit?

The scope of fire safety engineering can extend into the area of fire damage reporting and the assessment of the need and feasibility of repairs. Building surveyors carry out this role at present; might they be best fitted to continue it after being trained and educated in general building surveying? The degree of knowledge required in order to provide a comprehensive report on fire damage is wide, ranging as it does from basic construction knowledge related to building types, structures and materials, to the effect that fire and water have on them, to the best methods of repair in the light of economic considerations. At present the only way in which this knowledge can be gained is on a self-development basis. There are no recognised courses nor qualifications and it is up to the individual to study by consulting current literature and attending the relevant conferences or seminars. This theoretical knowledge needs to be applied in practice, yet in the absence of a definitive rationale it is likely that errors in judgement and mistakes in the application of fire safety measures may occur during the growth of expertise. In the meantime, all building disciplines should encourage a strong interest in the consideration of fire safety technology.

FURTHER FACTORS

Finally, in this discussion of fire technology, some general points will be raised in relation to the contextual factors which form the framework to this study.

Social attitudes and values

In developing and so-called 'developed' countries alike there is a public belief in the sanctity of life. This, coupled with a growth in materialism, is making people conscious of the need for fire safety. There is a public outcry when fire has caused a number of deaths and injuries, and improved measures are called for. This is not only true in the case of major, nationally reviewed fires, such as the Summerland Fire on the Isle of Man in 1973, but also in the case of smaller fires, with loss of life, occurring at a local level. In the wake of the Summerland Fire a public inquiry investigated its cause and analysed its propagation and consequences. A series of conclusions and subsequent recommendations arose from this, relating to the fire resistance of materials, the methods of construction used, the responsibility of the building's designers for the fire, and the responsibility of the building's managers.

A fire in a maisonette in Birmingham, which caused the death of a number of people in a family, is another example. Although the main reason for their deaths could be attributed to the fact that a blazing settee dragged towards the main access door obstructed escape, the concern of tenants in the same block and similar constructions forced the local authority landlord to set up additional fire safety measures, in particular the provision of means of escape. A further example is the case of Ronan Point, a multi-storey block of flats in London which suffered a gas explosion, causing the progressive collapse of one corner of the building. Tenants of that block, and others like it, expressed concern over its safety. This concern was also reinforced by professionals who viewed these forms of construction (and the *manner* in which they were constructed) as inherently unsafe. Remedial works were carried out to literally patch the building together and make it safer. Still, public confidence was not restored. To show the safety of the building it was decided to set fire to one of the flats, demonstrating the building's resistance to fire and the way in which the fire could be controlled. Suffice it to say that this demonstration did nothing to allay public and professional fears. Ronan Point was demolished. Public opinion is a powerful force and can directly influence aspects of building technology.

Economic Factors

Economic factors play a large part in all building technology decisions, and no less in the case of fire safety measures. To provide or to increase passive and active measures costs money. Consider the installation of sprinklers. In the first place there are some doubts regarding their reliabiity in the event of fire, and some lesser doubts, now being dispelled owing to research and statistical information, as to their worth in containing fire spread. In the light of this, building procurers will need to be convinced that sprinklers are economically viable and that their costs can be outweighed, in the event of fire, by their ability to reduce damage and save property. The life safety factor is not high, as this is generally related to the time elapsing between fire ignition and discovery (a time which can be reduced by the use of smoke or heat detectors). However, with an increase in the levels of awareness of a building's owner's duty of care, civil court cases could be brought claiming damages where it is considered that due precautions have not been taken. Payments in damages could be high and in the future these may need to be taken into consideration in assessing the costs of installation in relation to the costs of losses, both in property and in lives. At present, there is a strong economic factor influencing the provision of sprinklers: the level of fire insurance premiums. Insurance companies consider the building's fire safety measures as a whole system and assess the risk and levels of loss on this basis. Sprinkler systems have demonstrably reduced loss claims and, therefore, are seen by insurers as a means of reducing the fire hazard, thereby reducing the risk. In actuarial terms this means that premiums can be lowered.

There are also economic advantages to be gained by using trade-offs between active and passive systems. Although such trade-offs are scarce in the UK their employment should grow with the increase in fire safety knowledge. In Canada, for example, concessions are allowed on flame spread ratings for (a) wall and ceiling linings, (b) combustible roof construction floor areas for most building types, (c) the size of unprotected openings in external walls, (d) the interconnection of floor spaces in high-rise buildings, and (e) the travel distances for escape, applying to the use of sprinklers in high-rise buildings such as restaurants, department stores, garages and storage areas. This gives the designer greater flexibility in planning space, and produces savings in construction costs due to the reduction in fire resistance properties. With careful design and specification it might be possible to recover a major portion of sprinkler installation costs, as well as benefit from lower insurance premiums.

Legislation

The use of legislation is always contentious, and this is no less true for fire technology. No one can be said to welcome any legislation with open arms, but unfortunately there are people who *will* build unsafe structures. One would have thought that with the increase in the awareness of construction knowledge there should be less need for legislation to ensure its adoption. Unfortunately, the scope of legislation is keeping pace with the expansion of knowledge precisely because it is not effectively and comprehensively applied. Nearly all developed nations have detailed legislation covering fire safety in buildings, and some countries, notably the USA and Canada, offer guidance on the trade-offs between passive and active measures. Some nations recognise qualitative and quantitative assessments for fire safety. Malhotra (*Fire Safety in Buildings*, BRE report, 1987) has called for some amendments to the legislation in the UK. At present there are differences between various regions of the UK. Malhotra's main criticism is that the scope of the regulations is limited, and that they should be expanded to include all aspects of a fire safety system, including management. There is some justification for this, as although the building technologist must comply with practice recommendations and legislation, what happens after hand-over is poorly covered by legislation. In certain types of building, fire certificates are required which show that an inspection has been made (usually just prior to completion, after new build, alteration or refurbishment work). This certificate is granted indefinitely and there is no systematic follow-up procedure to ensure further compliance. It is the moral and ethical responsibility of the building owner to maintain the fire safety systems and to amend them with any subsequent change in circumstances. Experience has shown, usually in the form of disastrous fires, that this maintenance is often carried out inadequately. It may be necessary, therefore, to introduce legislation which enforces a higher regard to fire safety measures during occupation.

As previously mentioned, there is an anomaly in the approach of the regulations to means of escape; they are considered to be mandatory and separate from the other provisions relating to fire spread. This does not allow for the possibility of exploring interactions between measures. Again, means of escape legislation should be applied to *all* types of buildings. For example, two-storey houses in single occupation do not come within the scope of building types in the legislation, yet irrefutable statistical evidence (*Fire Statistics*, HMSO, published annually) shows that the majority of deaths occur in domestic situations. Perhaps this is another case for further legislation, undesirable though it may be in other respects.

Functional requirements

The functional requirements of a building, its structure, fabric and the materials utilised, fundamentally determine fire safety measures. New types of buildings demand a fresh look at fire safety. For example, an automated warehouse creates a very different set of circumstances to a multi-activity leisure centre, but both are relatively new developments. New materials are used to satisfy functional requirements, and with advances in technology they can meet several functional requirements. For example, the use of sprayed coatings to structural steel members can provide fire protection, corrosion resistance and a pleasing appearance.

Technological change and development

Technological change and development is continuous and will have considerable influence over the measures used in fire safety in the future. For instance, by using rapid-response sprinkler systems it could be possible to extend trade-offs between the constituent elements of the fire safety system. Advances in technology can, and are, creating computer-controlled systems covering all aspects of safety and security in buildings. These are likely to become more reliable and, therefore, more widespread. The use of pressurised smoke zones could also become widespread as more knowledge is gained regarding their behaviour, and as equipment is developed to maintain the correct conditions. In simple hand-held fire extinguishers the use of substances other than water or foam, such as Halon gas, is universal. As has already been remarked, technology can produce new equipment and substances to fight fires, but their effective use is often limited. The ability of the average person to operate equipment tends to be inversely proportional to its level of sophistication, so advances in technology need to be matched to advances in education, and training given in the use of new equipment and materials.

SUMMARY

It seems inevitable that advances in fire technology will be governed by catastrophe and controversy. History has shown that major advances in fire safety measures follow in the wake of major fires which usually result in injury and loss of life. This is still as true in the 1980s as it was in 1666. The science of fire is still in its infancy, but enough is now known to produce fire growth simulations for specific layouts and circumstances, so that designers can gain some insight into the effectiveness of their solutions in the event of fire. On this knowledge can be based an effective total fire safety system for a particular building. In the provision of these measures there needs to be a greater recognition of the possibilities of trade-offs between the various elements, and of the fact that the concept of fire safety engineering should be more widely employed.

At present in the UK there are a number of glaring anomalies in the detailed provisions and in the practice of fire resistance, as identified by Malhotra in his report. For example, he states that the current provisions for fire resistance and compartment sizes for the majority of low-rise buildings are in excess of those required solely for life safety purposes, but that in high-rise buildings and other complex structures, where total immediate evaluation is not feasible, higher levels of provision are justified. A further instance is the introduction of a new concept of 'limited combustibility' in the Approved Documents to the UK Building Regulations. Malhotra states that it is necessary to examine the *exact need* for the specification of non-combustible materials. It should be possible to limit the control of these materials to certain selected locations where hazardous conditions are expected to exist, such as near heating appliances. The concept of 'limited combustibility' should therefore be replaced by the concept of 'limited heat release'. For further thought-provoking comments on fire safety, see Malhotra's report.

Fire technology is influenced by the society in which it exists. A concern for safety felt by the general public can influence specific measures; concern for loss of property can initiate advances in fire fighting equipment development. A government, through legislation, can ensure that all building designers, builders and occupiers work to minimum requirements based on tests, simulations, analysis and experience. The role of the building professional in the future is likely to embrace a deeper concern for fire technology, and we may see the evolution of experts giving comprehensive advice on fire technology in relation to buildings and their use.

The range of issues and depth of knowledge contributing to fire technology is increasing, and this part of the book has only skated across the surface. One final point must be emphasised: in the general consideration of the technology of building, fire safety is of considerable importance. Its requirements and solutions have a profound influence over the layout, structure, materials used and construction details of all types of buildings, together with their location and function in society.

QUESTIONS

1. Discuss the advantages of 'trade-offs' for the building technologist.
2. Comment on the proposal for embracing all building types in

means of escape measures.
3. Should legislation follow or formulate fire safety measures?
4. Evaluate the total fire safety measures, including management aspects, of the building you occupy during a normal day.
5. Discuss the extent to which economic factors should influence the provision of safety measures preventing loss of life.

Part Four
SPECIFICATION

16. Introduction

One of the major ways in which the intentions of a designer can be communicated is by the written word. Construction details are mainly described by the use of drawings, but not all the necessary information can be included on limited sizes of paper, nor can it be fully explained by using notes or lines. Therefore, the use of words is inevitably required to augment the two-dimensional plan – in order to attempt a three-dimensional picture of the proposals. Despite many valiant attempts to produce phrases couched in clear and concise English there are still some problems in interpretation and suitability in use: these will be discussed in Chapter 19. Prior to this some aspects of the format and use of specifications will be presented. Common formats will be described and an explanation given of their basic content and development in Chapter 17. Chapter 18 will specifically look at bills of quantity: their format and content and their effective use. The final chapter in this part of the book will discuss the role of specifications and future trends.

WHAT IS A SPECIFICATION?

One definition of a specification is that it is *a concise statement of a set of requirements to be satisfied by a product, a material or a process, indicating, where appropriate, the procedure by means of which it may be determined whether the requirements are satisfied*. A dictionary definition might read: 'detailed description of construction, workmanship, materials, etc.'; and to specify might be 'to name expressly, mention definitely'. The first definition is open in its approach; it refers to a 'set of requirements', not merely, as in the dictionary definition, to a 'detailed description'. In construction terms this latter definition is too restricted and reflects only one type of specification. If the general 'set of requirements' is used as a basis for a specification, its underlying rationale can be centred on a choice of aspects. For example, the 'set of requirements' could be solely economic. The specification could be expressed in terms which state that each material, component or detail should meet the specified economic criteria. Alternatively, the set of requirements could be as indicated in the dictionary definition – a detailed description of the exact sizes, standards and fixing procedures.

To use an example, a construction detail, such as a fascia board to eaves, might have a specified cost of £X. A second specification could state that the fascia board is to be of softwood, size 200mm × 35mm, fixed with nails to the end of each joist. It might even stipulate the type or grade of softwood, and with this is seen an attempt to describe quality. A specification can try to cover a wide range of requirements, and in the above example, will give a full description, supply economic boundaries, and give information on the performance expectations of the fascia board. One method of expanding a specification from just a detailed description is to refer to other documents, such as Standards and Codes of Practice. Indeed, some specifications can be written comprised wholly of references to such documents. In this case, the user of the specification would need a copy of these standards in order to interpret the specified requirements.

DRAWING UP A SPECIFICATION

This in itself is a process of interpretation, as the specification writer has to refer back to and understand the intentions of a client. The designer's brief is the master document from which the design and construction information is determined. The manner in which this brief is ascertained and subsequently presented will influence not only the shape, size, materials, etc. of the finished building, but will also influence the type and scope of the specification. If the client's intentions are not clear, or the designer fails to interpret them accurately, the resulting specification will be inadequate. A common conflict centres on *quality* – considered in terms of economic factors and levels of possible achievement given particular tolerances and available skills. If the designer has not completely resolved such issues, his indecision will be reflected in the contract documentation, especially the specification, and can lead to variations in interpretation at tender or pricing stages. Subsequently, the builder may be working on a set of assumptions which do not match those of architect or client. This can lead to conflict during the construction process.

To sum up, the brief arising from discussions between designer and client should be based on clear and agreed intentions and be presented in such a manner that the specification writer is fully aware of the client's expectations and is able to express them clearly and concisely.

STANDARDS

The majority of specifications are based on standards; in industrialised nations these standards are published, and often directly referred to in building control. For example, as seen in Part Three of this volume, the means of escape provisions for designated building types in the UK are mandatory under the Building Regulations 1985, but the document gives direct reference to Codes of Practice and British Standards indicating the means by which the requirements can be met. Therefore production drawings must indicate these requirements in relation to construction details; the specification should refer to them, and perhaps give further information.

Standards are not a new development. There are examples of societies throughout history employing standards concerned with building. Documentary evidence has been found relating to the construction of buildings in codes surviving from the ancient city of Babylon. Dating from 2050 BC, this civil code deals with many aspects of civic life, including regulations on how a building should be constructed so that it can serve its purpose and endure for a reasonable period (perhaps the first performance criteria). The code specifies penalties for non-compliance.

In order to build up a set of requirements two elements are essential: a common system of weights and measures and a means of communicating the *meaning* of the system, usually by employing graphical or word-letter symbols. Evidence shows that in Roman times there was probably a higher level of standardisation in building components than that pertaining today (see Thomas, M.H., 'The Modular Reconstruction of Emona' in *Modular Quarterly*, 1964). The basis of unit length used was the human body, and Vitruvius, a Roman architect and engineer writing around 27 BC, stated that his most important doctrine was that major temples and buildings were to be designed with a certain measure of symmetry and proportion based on a well-shaped body. This harmony also had to be found in the relationship between the parts and the whole. The Japanese developed a dimensional system to suit the design of mats. This was again based on the human body's dimensions, and as the mats were laid on a floor to form a room, the walls enclosing the room became modules of these basic dimensions. Thus room and building sizes became standardised. In the UK, the common imperial size of brick – 8½″ × 4″ × 2½″ (now converted into its direct metric equivalent) – was first produced in the late 1470s. Its size was further regulated in Acts of Parliament in the period 1568 to 1625. In the USA in the late eighteenth century the first industrial standardisation took place, in the manufacture of arms. In the production of interchangeable parts, using division of labour arising from the need for mass production, a series of standard parts were made. This led to the making of machines to manufacture these parts; then, in order to achieve consistently correct sizes and qualities, these machines themselves needed to be standardised. From this the use of standard tests which ascertain the accuracy of either a good or a machine developed and is now common practice in industrialised nations.

Every nation develops its own sets of requirements. It is likely that these standards will then become standardised on an international scale. Chapter 17 will describe some universally used standards and discuss their evolution.

QUALITY

One of the main purposes of a specification is to set levels of quality. But what is quality? Pirsig is unsure, as this quotation from *Zen and the Art of Motorcycle Maintenance* shows:

Quality you know what it is, yet you don't know what it is. But that's self-contradictory. But some things are better than others, that is, they have more quality. But when you try to say what the quality is, apart from the things that have it, it all goes poof! There's nothing to talk about. But if you can't say what quality is, how do you know what it is, or how do you know that it even exists? If no one knows what it is, then for all practical purposes it doesn't exist at all. But for all practical purposes it really does exist. Why else would people pay fortunes for some things and throw others in the trash pile? Obviously some things are better than others . . . but what's the 'betterness'? So round and round you go, spinning mental wheels and nowhere finding any place to get traction. What the hell is quality? What is it?

This is a dilemma that the building specification writer attempts to resolve and make clear via the written word. In trying to define quality there must be constant reference to 'things', as Pirsig puts it. But this is ambiguous. Take the example of plastering, and base the discussion on Building Research Establishment Digest 213, May 1978, *Choosing specifications for plastering*. The Digest begins with a paragraph on the reasons for using a plaster finish, giving reasons such as (a) it is intended to conceal unevenness, (b) it may be required to improve fire resistance or (c) modify sound absorption or (d) mitigate the effects of condensation. It should provide a finish that is smooth, crack-free, hygienic, resistant to damage and easily decorated. Four stages in effecting the choice of plastering specifications are presented:

Stage 1: Choosing the finish (whether hard or soft, smooth or textured). The decorative coating and the drying time available are the main considerations here. Tables are presented in the Digest giving plastering systems suitable for various backgrounds and plaster finishes, along with the more important properties likely to determine their choice.

Stage 2: Deciding upon the number of coats. The Digest explains that the normal application for brickwork and blockwork is two coats, and on boards is one coat, with perhaps some preparation work. Some indication of thickness is given, but only in a range of 5mm to 25mm.

Stage 3: Deciding upon plaster undercoats. This section of the Digest is sub-divided into five parts. The first stresses the strength of the background, the second looks at the suction of the background with respect to strength, adhesion and quality of plasterwork; the third is concerned with the 'key' or bonding of plaster to background; the fourth considers drying, shrinkage and thermal movement with respect to the interaction between plaster and background; and the final part gives a short discussion of the problem of efflorescence.

Stage 4: Deciding upon the plastering specification. This section of the Digest gives further notes on the tables which should enable an appropriate type of finish to be selected for a given background.

The final paragraph of the Digest comments on the problems of cracking in joints between different backgrounds.

One table in the Digest relates the factors of (a) suction, (b) key or bond, (c) drying shrinkage to background, and (d) the suitable alternative undercoat plasters. Another table classifies the various plaster finishes and gives their characteristics. By following the stages set out in the Digest, with ultimate reference to the tables, the specification writer should be able to determine the type of plaster to be used, and its mix-ratios, if pertinent, relative to the background. This Digest is concerned with ensuring that the *right* plaster is selected for the set of requirements relating to background and finish, and although it discusses finish, cracking and quality it does not define what exactly is acceptable. Of course, the specification writer should further define the standard desired.

Some aspects of plastering can be defined. For example, the Digest refers to the 'grinning' through of joints occurring on block walls owing to differential suction. Where very wet, lightweight, aggregate concrete blocks are laid, and plastered soon after, an undercoat of lightweight gypsum-browning plaster tends to remain soft over the blocks but to stiffen over the joints, building up to a slightly greater thickness there as it is worked. The resulting difference in level is not normally corrected by the final coat and can be of the order of 1–2mm. But is this acceptable? Does this define quality? If the difference in level is 0.5mm, will that be of the right quality? While the Digest shows how a plaster finish can be successful applied, it still does not get to grips with a definition of quality. Nor, it is suggested, will the written specification.

Returning to the earlier example of the fascia board, assume that the specification states: 'the timber shall be free from knots'. If one knot is found, this will contravene the specification, but in all likelihood the supervising architect will give approval. Who, or what, is right? If over a two-metre length there are four knots, is this acceptable? In the case of plaster finish, is a hair-line crack around a door frame where it meets the plaster and is not covered by an architrave, acceptable, of the right quality? If the crack is 1mm wide, is this unacceptable? How many specifications actually specify? Here, to specify would be to state that cracks over a certain thickness are unacceptable, or more than x number of hairline cracks per metre square are unacceptable. A typical traditional specification clause on plasterwork states:

If the material is not dealt with by a BS or Code of Practice, state its size, thickness and quality. Quality is the most difficult to define and it may be necessary to refer to the standard range of a manufacturer, e.g. . . . to be from Semtex Ltd range C or of equal quality. Remember that 'equal' means equal in the eyes of the architect, so in general the contractor will play safe and price Semtex range C.

A number of points can be made here. First, there is an acknowledgement that quality is difficult to define, so why use loose terminology? Second, in naming a manufacturer the specification is immediately limited; why not provide a list of possible suppliers for each material? Third, money alone cannot define quality; it can give value or worth to an object or service, but that object or service is not in itself appraised solely on cost criteria. Something seen as being of high quality can have a lower cost than that of a highly priced article. Price is normally governed by market forces, especially in capitalist societies, and so value to the purchaser is a major consideration.

Quality is usually judged initially on finish, on what something looks like. In the case of plastering a common phrase used in specifications is 'true and level', referring to the plaster surface. Additionally, this may be further described as needing to be 'trowelled hard and smooth with a steel float'. Now, what is 'true and level', and what is 'smooth'? These words are subjective in that they describe a state which is dependent upon an individual's observations and perceptions, not upon scientific objective data. Therefore, in the final analysis, they are quite likely to become an issue for dispute. This is alluded to in the extract from the book on specification writing: if an 'equal' substitute is used it must satisfy the architect, for he (or whoever is the assessor of the work) determines the degree of quality. What is 'smooth'? If a hand is lightly run over a plaster surface and some slight (what is 'slight'?) undulations are felt, is this then 'uneven'? If these undulations, although felt, do not show visibly, can this be taken as an acceptable criterion of 'smoothness'? The placing of an artificial light source along the plaster surface will give shadows if interrupted by bumps, ridges or wrinkles. In natural and overhead artificial light these shadows will not be displayed, but undoubtedly the surface could be perceived as not being 'smooth', 'true' and 'level'. This situation may arise on site, leading to disagreement over the acceptability of a plaster finish. The clerk of works may argue that the finish does not meet the requirements of the specification. The contractor may argued that in normal usage any minor irregularities would neither show nor affect the application of a decorative finish, and that the job was carried out with the specified materials, with good workmanship, and was necessarily done to the price quoted in the accepted tender. The latter point echoes the old adage, 'you only get what you pay for!'. This is an unsatisfactory state of affairs.

Performance Specifications

The construction industry is aware of the shortcomings in specifications written in general terms, and initiatives are being pursued which aim to make clients' or designers' intentions and expectations both clearer and more concise. Arising from these developments is a broad classification. Those specifications written in terms which clearly point to one construction solution, with materials named, sizes given, and perhaps even suppliers named, are within the traditional category. The newer range of specifications are based on terms which describe what the material, construction detail or component is expected to do and how it must behave during and after placement; these are categorised as *performance specifications*. A detailed description of performance specifications is given in Part Two of *Building Technology 3*, in this series. Here only a brief account will be given.

In the first place a comprehensive body of standards must exist upon which performance can be measured. As buildings are designed for the use of humans these standards are based on the physiological requirements of people and the functional performance of materials, space, form and construction details that will satisfy both human needs and the long-term life expectations of the fabric and structure. In the earlier part of this volume, emphasis was placed on the need to create a building which meets the demands of prevailing climatic conditions and forms an internal environment which allows the occupiers healthily and comfortably to carry out their activities. Using this perception, the building envelope may be seen as a climatic barrier, acting as the interface between the internal and external environment. It is through performance specification that the functional data on the properties and characteristics of materials and construction details can be fully exploited to provide technological solutions which can effectively satisfy requirements.

A degree of flexibility must be manifest, as the specification will not necessarily prescribe a solution but will lay down criteria which need to be met. For example, in a traditional specification a window may be fully described, in terms of materials, size, number of opening lights, thickness of glazing and size of individual members; a particular brand from a named manufacturer might be specified. A performance specification, however, will take a wider view and try not to be prescriptive in the final choice but ensure that the choice made is based on a range of criteria which meet the requirements of function, use, cost and maintenance. In the case of the window, the performance requirements might be: (a) to achieve a stated reduction in noise levels; (b) to have a defined resistance to heat loss; (c) to be cleanable from the inside; (d) to meet fire resistance requirements; (e) to be able to provide a level of natural ventilation; (f) to have a maintenance clear period of a stated number of years, and so on. Additionally, aesthetic criteria may be laid down, reflecting the desired architectural style of the building and the designer's intentions. A range of windows from many manufacturers could meet these requirements and the builder and architect together will select the most appropriate, using criteria such as availability, cost and buildability. This type of specification fully utilises the ever-growing body of knowledge on the performance of building materials and components. It allows for the optimum selection of materials, using the knowledge of many interested parties, and the up-to-date utilisation of innovative products. In order to provide guidance in the preparation of performance standards in building a Master List of Properties has been produced, with some shortened versions relating to particular groups of products. This facilitates an easier comparison of their properties.

The Building Regulations 1985 have recognised the value of performance-related sets of requirements by giving credibility to the use of Agrément Certificates as a means of showing that products have, and are, meeting performance standards. Agrément Certificates are described in the next chapter, along with other standards.

In this introduction to the concept of specifications a number of questions relating to quality and to the link between function and description have been left hanging in the air. Discussion of these will be continued in Chapter 19. Many standards are used as a basis for specifications in the construction industry, and these will be described in the next chapter.

QUESTIONS

1. Using an example from your experience, describe the use of the specification in the process of construction.
2. Look at a number of clauses from a specification and critically examine them for clarity of intention.
3. Discuss the criteria upon which a specification should be based.

17. Standards

THE NATURE OF STANDARDS

Standards can be placed in one of two groups: (a) that of *fundamental standards*, dealing with basic units, terminology, symbols, methods of measurement and classification, and (b) that of *applied standards* dealing with the quality of materials, products and components, with methods of testing, sampling and controlling quality, and with codes of practice for design construction and maintenance. A further sub-division may indicate the origin of a standard, whether from natural standardisation or from organised standardisation. The former is the result of the growth of a habit, custom or tradition. The latter refers to standards which have resulted from planning; most building standards fall into this category. Most standards are technically based, giving methods of testing. Those standards which give details of how the building work shall be executed or who shall inspect the work come within the class of *managerial standards* (as do the majority of the UK Codes of Practice).

A standard must satisfy one or more of the following requirements: dimensional, functional, quality and interchangeability (see Fig. 4.1). Where there is an overlap denoting agreement or compatibility then a degree of interchangeability can be engineered. The problem of quality is again raised here, and in relation to building products Nugarajan gives the following definition (Nugarajan, R., *Standards in Building*, Pitman, 1977):

A degree of goodness in material, performance, durability, etc. It is also a general term synonymous with property . . . in fact it covers a wide range of meanings. So far as standardisation is concerned, quality, as a rule, refers to the characteristics and appearance of a product including purity, colour and texture as viewed by the consumer. This may be called 'consumer quality'. In principle, quality applies not only to performance and reliability in practical applications, but equally to safety in use and accuracy of dimensions.

Quality can also be seen as graded and it is possible to devise and agree levels of quality for materials and components. In the case of concrete, one criterion of quality – perhaps its most important – is *strength*. This can be assessed by testing samples 28 days after mixing and placing. It is possible to measure levels of quality by other specific performance criteria such as *thermal transmittance* or

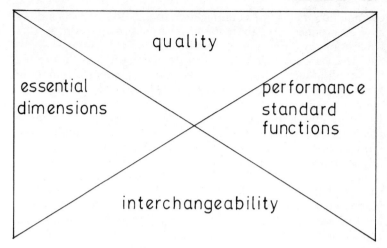

Fig. 4.1   *Requirements for standards*

fire resistance, but a product can meet these requirements and still be perceived as of a different quality to another demonstrating the same performance figures. There must be something else which denotes quality, and this may be related to the perceptions of the consumer, as alluded to by Nagarajan.

Interchangeability is the capability of a material or component to be exchanged for an exact copy or reproduction. Taking the concept further, it may be exchanged for a different product or component altogether. The point can be illustrated by installing a replacement door with the same size, characteristics and appearance as the original, or by using a door of completely different material, performance and appearance. Interchangeability implies that no physical changes are needed in order to accommodate the exchange.

The evolution of any one standard can be seen as a combination of three factors: *Subject* refers to a particular construction unit; the manner in which a standard can be manifested is its *Aspect*; its *Level* of acceptance ranges from the individual to the international.

Standardisation

Arising from the development of standards is the concept of standardisation. This goes further than producing a standard which can be utilised in a specification. The implication of standardisation is that materials, components, internal space and services are 'rationalised' into a set of discrete entities. For example, doors may be manufactured in only four sizes, windows may be produced in only ten styles, or the optimum size for the living room in a four-person family house may be fixed at 4m × 5m. There are fears that the use of standards will inevitably bring 'standardisation' in its wake. The aims of standardisation in construction are laudable nonetheless, hoping to achieve maximum overall economy in terms of cost, human effort, time and the consumption of scarce materials. Standardisation also aims at the maximum convenience in use, leading to simplification, rationalisation, variety reduction and consequently the interchangeability of building products. In the reaching of a standard it is likely that this will provide a good solution to a particular construction problem, especially as it will have been based on research and development. The creation of a standard will give a level of quality only if it is based on quantitative analysis. If this agreement on quality is reached then it can become an effective means of communicating intentions between client, designer and builder.

There is an inexorable trend towards more standards in industrialised nations, both within and across national borders. As new research, development and practice gains popular credibility the pressure for a standard to be set arises. Manufacturers, specifiers and consumers look for common ground upon which a product or material can be founded: they all need to be able to agree equally on what is acceptable. A standard will be able to lay down criteria for a product, and, if appropriate, it will indicate methods and give data that will verify the criteria. As manufacturers and specifiers expand their interests, and especially where countries form trading and economic communities such as the European Economic Community, they will need to satisfy the demands of partner nations. It is likely that either standards will not exist, or that where they do they will be in conflict. The former case would allow the formulation of a standard to be undertaken on an international level, acceptable to all the partners in its development. In the latter case, negotiations would have to be carried out to resolve the differences, producing, it would be hoped, a standard reflecting the best possible set of requirements.

A number of groups of standards will now be considered, with an outline of their means of preparation and their role in the UK. The three prime groups come under the auspices of the British Standards Institution; namely British Standards, Codes of Practice and Quality Assurance. The Agrément Certificates issued by the British Board of Agrément will also be discussed.

BSI STANDARDS

British Standards

These are technical documents which aim to save time; money, materials and energy in the production and exchange of goods and services. Implied within the standards is the notion of an acceptable quality obtainable at an acceptable cost; they define features which will ensure a product or service is fit for its purpose. A further aim of a standard is to promote safety, which implies a definition of what is acceptable at a reasonable level of risk. There are hundreds of standards covering the whole range of materials and products in construction. These are listed and briefly described in Smith, M. (ed.), *Manual of British Standards in Building Construction and Specification*, British Standards Institution Hutchinson, 1985. Each standard is prefixed with 'BS' and given a number or a part number if published in several sections. The year of publication is also given. For example: 'BS 1197 Concrete Flooring Tiles and Fittings Part 2: 1973 Metric Units'. This standard covers hydraulically pressed flooring tiles made with cement and aggregate. The tiles may be plain or coloured, matt or polished. Specifications for cement, pigments, aggregate additives and admixtures are given. Shape, finish, uniformity of colour and the various tolerances are specified. A standard may state the method by which the activity is to be performed and how conclusions are to be drawn, either by calculation or empirically. Standardised methods of sampling, measurement, testing, analysing and specifying are given.

Codes of Practice

These are a type of standard which recommends accepted good practice as followed by competent practitioners. They bring together the results of practical experience and scientific investigation in a form which enables technologists to make use both of existing practices and new developments. Two types of codes may be distinguished: one details professional knowledge or practice; the other is more specific, and may be referred to directly in a job specification by giving the code relating to a particular material and/or construction method. The codes are written for guidance only and are not to be seen as a source of objective criteria upon which compliance can be judged. The solutions given are not necessarily prescriptive or exclusive, but they could be used as a comparative base for alternative procedures or materials.

There are three categories of standards: British Standards (BS), Published Documents (PD) and Drafts for Development (DD).

The BS is the formal document giving the set standard. It is envisaged that the prefix 'CP' (for Codes of Practice) will eventually disappear and all definitive documents will have the prefix 'BS'. Published Documents are often issued to provide guidance or supplementary information. A Draft for Development is published when insufficient information or data is yet available, or because the subject is new. These can be seen as precursors to a British Standard and will be amended and added to in the course of time.

The standards are prepared by technical committees, whose members are those people who demonstrate a particular interest in the subject, with, it is to be hoped, a wide representation from industry, trades, professions and government departments. A BS should be in the national interest and be based on authoritative opinion, so the technical committee should take account of all significant viewpoints. Proposals for revisions to existing standards or the creation of new ones can be put forward by any responsible body. An initial draft is prepared, preferably from outside the committee, by a single person or a small panel. This draft standard is then issued for public comment and announced in *BSI News*. All comments received are reviewed by the technical committee, and when consensus has been reached the chairperson records approval. All standards undergo a review at least once every five years to determine whether a revision is needed.

This work is financed by the sales of publications, by voluntary subscriptions and by a government grant which matches subscription income.

Quality Assurance

Unfortunately, in buildings more defects and failures arise from inadequacies in the treatment of products at the design or construction stage than arise from inherent problems in the products themselves. The use of satisfactory products conforming to the relevant British Standards is not alone sufficient; the products must also be incorporated into the design and construction procedures in a proper manner. The quest for quality must involve *all* of those concerned with a building, and they must be fully aware of the most effective uses of products, materials and methods.

Two approaches may be taken to ensure the quality of a product or service. First, awarding a certificate will assure that a product has been manufactured to the highest levels of quality. The manufacturer employs a system of checks and controls which ensures that at various stages during the manufacturing process a product meets the correct standards. The emphasis here is on control practices and procedures. In the case of an organisation offering a service, for example an architectural or quantity surveying practice (or a building company), an independent assessment can be made of the organisation's own regulatory controls and checks, ensuring that its work is carried out to the highest standards, meeting the demands of a client in a technically competent manner, and giving value for money. Already, a number of professional practices have sought and obtained what are known as Quality Assurance assessments.

The Quality Assurance Division is a self-financing branch of the British Standards Institution whose operations have proved popular. It is likely that soon the majority of forward-thinking professional practices will seek Quality Assurance assessments, and that they may even require them in order to tender for public sector contracts or to supply goods. As society becomes more aware that good quality is obtainable, and can be ensured by the award of a Quality Assurance certificate, the discerning client will choose those practitioners who undertake assessment by the BSI.

AGRÉMENT CERTIFICATE

The British Board of Agrément is an independent testing and assessing body. Manufacturers of components and materials submit their products to the board for assessment of the initial integrity of the item with regard to its suitability in a building. A series of tests are carried out to verify the manufacturer's claims and it is monitored over a period of time while in use in a building. It is assessed in its normal working environment, not in a laboratory. According to the nature of the material or product appropriate tests are carried out. In other words, the *functions* of the product are ascertained, as well as its performance over a period of time. This is an advance on the equivalent British Standard, which lays down criteria only for the initial integrity of the product. Take for example the previously mentioned concrete flooring tiles. The BSI sets the standards and specifications for the manufacture of the tiles. A manufacturer could submit his tiles to the Agrément Board to verify their compliance to the BS 1197: Part 2: 1973, which could additionally show that they satisfy other performance criteria, such as 'freedom from slipperiness', 'resistance to abrasion' or 'ability to resist a range of chemicals'. The award of an Agrément Certificate denotes that the manufacturer's tiles are suited to use in particular situations with respect to the tested and verified performance criteria. The manufacturer can then state in technical and sales literature that, for instance, his tiles are suitable in a laboratory.

The Agrément Certificate is usually valid for a five-year period during which the board's inspectors continuously monitor the performance of the material or product. If the product fails to meet one or a number of performance criteria the certificate may be withdrawn. This threat was one reason for the initially slow increase in numbers of certificates applied for, as manufacturers are naturally worried that the damage to their reputations could be great in the event of a non-renewal of a certificate. Perhaps it is better not to submit to testing them to initially meet the requirements but fail them later. This situation is changing, however, with a rapid increase in the numbers of certificates sought and awarded. The catalyst for this change has been the Building Regulations 1985, in the manual of which specific reference is made to the British Board of Agrément. The essence of this reference is that approving authorities should take the granting of an Agrément Certificate as demonstrating that a material or component is fit for its purpose.

Certificates now contain detailed comments regarding a product's ability to meet the relevant requirements of the Building Regulations as described in the Approved Documents. The information on a certificate is given thus: the relevant Building Regulation clause is cited, together with comments on its interpretation and the extent to which the product meets its requirements. The Approved Documents present only one set of criteria, however, and the Building Regulations are couched in terms which allow other 'reasonable' or 'satisfactory' means of meeting requirements. This ought to encourage the development of new products and construction methods based on reliable research and development programmes. The awarding of an Agrément Certificate should give the seal of approval to these new products.

The Agrément Certificate also lists the tests carried out on the product and details the manner in which they were executed. It also gives the results, in general terms. Where particular aspects of a product were not tested, the certificate will state this. General comments regarding the product's suitability (or otherwise) for specified situations is given. Comments regarding installation according to manufacturer's instructions, as well as workmanship, are also to be included on the certificate. The following is a description of the information given on a BBA Certificate issued in March 1987 for an external sheeting product. The first item refers to the Building Regulations 1985, and comments are made regarding the compliance of the product to clauses A1, Loading; B4, External Fire Spread, External Walls; C4, Resistance to Weather and Ground Moisture; Regulation 7, Materials and Workmanship. In addition reference is made to clauses in the Building Standards (Scotland) Regulations 1981 to 1986, and to the Building Regulations (Northern Ireland) 1977. A technical specification includes a basic description of the product and details factors relating to safe delivery and safe handling on site. The Design Data section gives information to designers regarding the product's properties – listing, for example, other materials to which it can be fixed, its coefficient of expansion, and its strength and stability (reference is made here to BS 8200: 1985 Code of Practice for the design of non-load-bearing external vertical enclosures of buildings). Its properties in relation to fire are detailed, again with reference to the British Standards (namely BS 476: Part 5 and Part 6, 1968: Part 7, 1971). Thermal insulation is presented as a thermal conductivity figure. Durability is assessed to be in excess of 30 years, but it is estimated that sealed joints will require renewal at more frequent intervals, that there will also be a slight initial dulling of surface, and that there should be no maintenance required to the actual sheeting.

The section of the certificate concerning installation considers general good practice and describes procedures. A summary is given of all the technical investigations undertaken by the board to test the veracity of the manufacturer's claims. In addition, mention is made of further investigations carried out – a user survey and regular factory inspections to ensure that quality control is adequate. It is noted that any modifications made were satisfactory and that, finally, no failures of the product have been reported to the BBA.

Under the Conditions of Certification the BBA states that the product has been awarded a certificate for an unlimited period, provided that the specification remains unchanged and that the manufacturer continues to have the product checked by the BBA. The product is assessed under the various Acts, Regulations, Statutory Instruments, Codes of Practice and British Standards pertaining at the time of issue of the certificate. The certificate does not confirm or deny the presence or absence of patent rights. A specific reference is made to its safe use, but this is to be seen as minimum and does not in any way purport to restate the Health and Safety at Work Act 1974. It also states that there is a need for common law duties of care. Naturally, the BBA cannot be held responsible to any person or body for any loss or damage incurred in respect of personal injury arising as a direct or indirect result of the use of the product.

The Agrément Certificate builds upon British Standards and assesses the product in place and in use. Checks are carried out on the manufacturer's own tests, and the specifiers of the product are directed to the relevant British Standards to ensure that the product is properly integrated with other construction details and that the correct installation procedures are adopted. By giving the thermal conductivity of the sheeting the total heat loss through the wall of the construction can be ascertained. Joint design is specifically mentioned – to ensure integrity. Its behaviour in fire is stated as meeting the relevant British Standards, and it is deemed suitable for use in situations where Clause B4 of the Building Regulations 1985 applies. In order to aid the specifier and the preparer of construction drawings, the certificate also supplies drawings of details such as fixings and joints. These augment the written word and give a visual indication of standard details. A point to note is that the BBA widens its appraisal of the product to include a user survey. In this case the product had been manufactured and used previously and could be assessed after some years. The BBA contacted these users and questioned them about the fitness for purpose and the behaviour of the external sheeting. This aspect of the work of the BBA is important, as it can be a real measure of worth of the product.

The British Board of Agrément is a member of The European Union of Agrément (UEA) which is growing in status within the European Economic Community. A continuing series of technical committee sessions has begun to make significant progress in the rationalisation of standards with relation to Agrément Certificates. It is likely that the European Economic Commission will also issue directives putting pressure on member countries to seek common standards and approaches. This should mean that a product meeting the requirements of a member country Agrément Board will be acceptable throughout the Community.

An example of the possibility of products and systems being acceptable in all countries is the recent acknowledgement in the UK of unvented hot water systems. This was first allowable under the Building Regulations 1985, and in 1987 the first Agrément Certificate was issued in the UK for an unvented system. There is still some controversy over the safe use of these systems, and it will be interesting to see whether they become common. Following the award of certificates which meet all countries' requirements a manufacturer has access to a much larger potential market, and in order to maintain or increase market share a competent business will have to respond to initiatives such as that of the BBA.

British Standards, Quality Assurance and Agrément Certificates represent three separate routes to quality control but there is now a definite link between them. The link has been forged by the Building Regulations 1985 which make specific reference to British Standards and Agrément Certificates. In the awarding of an Agrément Certificate the board considers the quality control procedures of the manufacturer, and those submitting to a Quality Assurance Scheme will undoubtedly be considered as meeting BBA criteria. There is a further recognition of the need for effective installation within the Building Regulations in Schedule 7, Materials and Workmanship. (In the example of external sheeting the Agrément Certificate mentioned that the product should comply with Schedule 7.) Unfortunately, the wording of this document is unspecific, stating that materials and workmanship should conform to 'reasonable' and 'acceptable' standards. As this is now a requirement under the Building Regulations, where Codes of Practice, British Standards and Agrément Certificates exist for a product or practice, the levels of quality described in them should be achieved. Thus the wording of these documents should be *specific*, laying down quality levels and standards. These laid-down levels must be 'reasonable' and 'acceptable', satisfying the requirements of Schedule 7.

There is a complex cross-referencing between all the various documents discussed above, with the general intention of promoting the achievement of good standards and quality. This concern for quality reflects a more general quest for increasing standards and levels of quality in products and buildings. This topic is discussed in *Building Technology 1* in connection with the basic comfort and amenity levels within buildings. Where once the occupier was satisfied with open fires and uninsulated walls, now people in industrialised nations demand central heating and heavily insulated structures to reduce heat loss. There is a distinction to be made between standards and quality, because a rise in standards need not necessarily be seen as a rise in quality. A central heating system can be inefficient, costly or difficult to control owing to the poor quality of specification and design. The occupier may not be any more comfortable than if an open fire was used in each room. This aspect of the notion of quality will be discussed further in Chapter 19.

QUESTIONS

1. Select a British Standard (or equivalent national standard) relating to building and describe how it determines the specification of a material or product.
2. Discuss the desirability of all products having an Agrément Certificate.
3. Describe how a Quality Assurance Scheme can help a designer in the preparation of drawings and specifications for building work.
4. Analyse the relationships between British Standards, Quality Assurance Schemes and Agrément Certificates, and discuss their effect upon the construction process.

18. Bills of Quantity

STANDARD METHODS OF MEASUREMENT

One of the most important documents upon which a contractor bases his price is the bill of quantity. The bill of quantity originated in the UK and is now employed worldwide, although its use in other countries is not common. This document came into its own after the first *Standard Methods of Measurement* (*SMM*) was published in the early 1920s. The *SMM* laid down guidelines and rules for a common method of measuring dimensions, recording them and properly describing the work activity, material or component. In so describing the measured work a specification is defined.

The prime objective of a bill of quantity is to provide a common document upon which a number of builders can base their prices when tendering in competition for building work. All builders may then base their price on exactly the same quantities of materials required. It is not necessary for them to work out their own quantities from the drawings, thus saving work and reducing tender costs. It is not unusual for a bill of quantities to be supplemented by a normal specification, but usually all major clauses and items are included within the bill.

There are various ways in which work required can be measured and presented in the bill of quantity. It may contain a 'preambles' section giving the job description and detailing special conditions, the degree to which work is to be carried out to the relevant standards, levels of workmanship, and so on. Subsequent sections on the separate trades of the plasterer, bricklayer, painter and decorator, or contractor may detail each item of work with its own brief description and measure. Alternatively, the document may be divided into sections according to the form of the building project: for example, Phase 1, Phase 2; or House Type A, House Type B. In the case of refurbishment or alteration work the document may be divided according to floors or sections of the building. Broad divisions such as 'ground works', 'superstructure', 'finishings' and 'services' could be used to define the basic layout. Specification clauses pertinent to the trade, section or type may be placed prior to the measured descriptions, with or without preamble.

In order to achieve a common building language, and an

accurate interpretation of that language, the editions of the *Standard Methods of Measurement* are specific about how an item should be measured and what should be stated in its description. This description is not sufficient to convey the full specification, and either it will need to be expanded in the description of the items or a full and clear description will be placed in the preambles. Two reference documents will be discussed here which purport to provide this additional information.

The first is known as 'Fletcher and Moore', after its authors, L. Fletcher and T. Moore, but its true title is *Standard Phraseology for Bills of Quantities* (four volumes, published by George Godwin Ltd, 4th Edition, 1979). This is directly based on the *Standard Method of Measurement* rules and shows the sub-division of each item, in various stages, in order to give the basic measured description. It states what should be included in the bill of quantities. Based on a traditional approach to specification, it does not really expand upon the degree of description already presented in the *SMM*, although it enables the person preparing the bill of quantities to easily locate an item and then quickly ascertain the factors relating to its classification. For example, excavation to reduced levels is determined in stages of depth commencing from ground level. These stages are clearly presented in the guide so the measurer can locate classifications at a glance and select those appropriate to the job requirements.

NATIONAL BUILDING SPECIFICATION

The second reference document is particularly concerned with ensuring that the specification element of the bill of quantities is clearly and concisely presented with respect to the quality intentions of the designer, architect or surveyor. This document is the *National Building Specification*, published by National Building Specification Ltd, sponsored by the Royal Institute of British Architects. It is a library of standard clauses or preamble clauses and not a standard specification. It presents many direct alternatives. All the clauses are optional, which allows selection to suit the individual designer's intentions. The clauses are grouped under the CI/SfB classification system, and the loose leaf document is divided into commodity and workmanship clauses. The code for each clause is also used to group and locate items and is intended to be used as cross-reference with the bill of quantities and to the contract drawings. There is a heavy reliance on British Standards as the basis for specification and quality.

As each clause has a reference number this can be utilised in computer-generated specifications. The applicable clause reference is entered, and as the full specification data is held in store, the relevant clause can be recalled and printed to form the complete specification for the job.

The authors say that there are a number of advantages in the use of the *NBS* and they have grouped them under the headings of 'designers', 'drawings', 'schedules of work' and 'builders'. Under a standard form of contract the architect is responsible for the specification, even though it may be prepared by someone else, a quantity surveyor for example. The *NBS* confronts the specification writer with a comprehensive series of questions about the materials to be used and how they are to be assembled. Its clauses are an authoritative source of technical guidance which will also control and standardise the choice of materials and techniques. This should lead to an improvement in the reliability and suitability of the resulting buildings.

By using the *NBS* reference system a cross-matching can be achieved between drawings and specification. The drawing details can be annotated with the reference code; this reduces the number of words cluttering the drawing, and relates the intention to the relevant specification clause. In the preparation of the working drawings it is necessary also to develop the specification order to designate the appropriate clauses. This will aid decision-making, as it requires the architect to address the problem of standards and quality while engaged on the detailed design of drawings. This should bring about a consistent match between drawings and specification.

When the specification is used in the bill of quantities it can aid the estimator by its depth of specification clause and its system of referencing. Each part can be easily found by either arranging the specification and measured items in the same order or systematically cross-referencing the measured item headings to the specification. It is also possible to combine the two arrangements.

The *NBS* can be used in conjunction with schedules of work. The schedules should contain a minimum number of words to identify clearly each kind of work, again with the use of cross-references. Any additional information should be placed within the schedule if not contained in the specification or drawings, especially if it is not able to be accommodated in the general clauses. The schedule can be laid out room by room for alterations or renovations, or by different trades for new work or refurbishment.

It is claimed that the *NBS* can help both the tenderer and the builder. At the tender stage a clear indication of standards and quality can be obtained, so the price can realistically match the architect's intentions. At the building stage the *NBS* will help in ordering the right materials and components, and as these are directly referred to on the drawings, it will expedite the ordering process. The advantages of using a well defined specification include the probability that it will reduce the number of on-site disputes caused by ambiguity of meaning. Time will be saved by the builder because there is less need to chase the architect for information as it already appears on drawings and specification. There should be fewer variations because detailed decisions have been taken prior to tender, which should lead to fewer changes of mind by the architect, with a consequent reduction in disruptions. Quality control should be less arbitrary than with traditional specifications. With a clearer definition, the task of control becomes easier for builder and architect.

To explore the idea of quality further an analysis of a typical *NBS* clause should consider whether 'quality' is defined. Taking the example of plaster finish already discussed (see pp.180–82), the works version of the *NBS* offers the following clauses, amongst others, as choices:

(a) Accuracy – finish surfaces to a true plane to correct line and level, with all angles and corners to a right angle unless otherwise specified, and with walls and reveals plumb and square.
(b) Accuracy of plaster 13mm thick or more: maximum permissible gap between an 1800mm, straight edge and any point on the surface to be 3mm.
(c) Smooth plaster finish: trowel to float to produce a tight, matt, smooth surface with no hollows, abrupt changes in level or trowel marks. Do not use water brush and avoid excessive trowelling and over-polishing.

The wording of these clauses is clear and prescriptive. For example, in clause (c) there is a specific reference to the manner in which the finish is to be achieved, with an instruction *not* to do something; there are to be no hollows or abrupt changes, so in the example previously mentioned the problem of ridges caused at joints between blocks and mortar must clearly be solved. A method is given to assess the accuracy of plaster using a straight edge, which implies that there can be differences in levels up to 3mm over the plaster surface. Here a direct quantifiable standard is given which can be easily tested. There is no reason for a specifier not to give another measurement for the permissible gap, either greater or less than that proposed. The gap given is based on experience of what is possible for a competent plasterer using common materials.

On balance it must be stated that the *NBS* gives a clear definition on standards and levels of quality, and its increasing use by architects and specifiers demonstrates its applicability to present expectations and practices.

The bill of quantities has come under attack from people both inside and outside the building industry. Its relevance is questioned, together with the costs involved in its production. In many cases it is superseded during the construction work; it has also been found wanting in the provision of clear details regarding materials and standards of workmanship. Its critics point to the fact that the great majority of industrialised nations do not use such documents. The responsibility for ascertaining the correct amount of materials required for a particular job at tender stage is left to the contractor. The British Property Federation in the UK has been particularly critical of the role of the bill of quantities, and in their proposals for a new form of building contract they dispense with them completely.

Putting aside the questions of cost and contractual suitability, the bill of quantities has been found to be lacking in its definition of technological issues. As it is produced at a relatively early stage in the design process, and is the result of a designer's perspective, it necessarily gives a set of prescriptions. In other words it presents the answers to questions without indicating what those questions were – as these have been already resolved during the design process. Many builders and specialist trade contractors have a wealth of current knowledge and experience which could be employed, first, in asking the right questions and, second, in assessing feasible choices at the time of tender. The opportunity for exploiting the technological expertise of a wide range of people is lost when a bill of quantities is produced which gives little or no chance for change, especially at the tender stage. While it is desirable to be sure that each competitor is tendering on a like basis, basic cost is but one aspect considered by clients. The growth of quality assurance, fast-track building, management fee projects, performance specifications and alternative contractual arrangements shows that both industry and society are demanding a wider measure of responsibility to be placed on the people involved in the process of construction. Technological decisions can be effectively made without the use of a bill of quantities, and, moreover, if performance specifications are used there is no need for a common bill of quantities, as the responsibility for meeting performance and quantity measures is solely that of the competing contractors. They will be expected to meet the highest standards, using the right amounts of materials and types of components commensurate with performance criteria based on the function of the finished product and the methods of construction employed.

The bill of quantities will have a part to play in the definition of technical details, but close attention needs to be paid to the specification element in order to give the builder a document which can be used effectively and confidently when the contract has been awarded.

QUESTIONS

1. Consider a section of a specification in a bill of quantities available to you, and criticise it with respect to its ability to impart clear technological information.
2. Comment on the use of the *NBS* system with respect to computer-generated bills of quantity.

19. The Role of Specifications

In this final chapter on specifications a number of issues will be addressed, beginning with a general discussion based on a CIOB paper looking at specification and purchasing. This discussion will be widened to consider the general role of specifications, and future trends in their use and format. Finally the issue of *quality* in construction will be addressed as an intertwining theme, first introduced in the introductory chapter of this volume, and underpinning our attitudes to technology, work and study.

SPECIFICATION AND PURCHASING

The CIOB Technical Information Paper No. 82, 1981, *Specification and purchasing within traditional contracting*, written by R.F. Moore, is based on research into the point at which the decision to use a clearly definable product is taken. The findings suggest that builders are responsible for major portions of project specification, either by design or by default, and that there is a lack of commitment on the part of many professionals to undertake their responsibilities. Many design tasks and specifications, it was found, are devolved to specialist sub-contractors and suppliers.

The CIOB study considers the four areas of contract documentation (primarily its content), product identification, quality of information and project perceptions. Moore found that in contract documentation the standards employed on drawings and in specifications have remained visibly low over a ten-year period. Content, consistently, has little relevance to actual needs, and this is most noticeable in bills of quantity (see the previous chapter). Drawings are riddled with mistakes and omissions, and specifications do not make up for these errors. It is little wonder, therefore, that many contractors fail to take specifications seriously. It appears that documents are purely used for the purposes of recording and do not contribute to the building project itself.

The majority of items in the finishing trades are described with reference to British Standards and Codes of Practice, which is felt to be sufficient by the designers. Unfortunately, this does lead to inappropriate specifications and drawings. This means that it is the builder who carries the burden of making the final specification decision. There is evidence of poor quality decisions made in mundane, though major, areas such as fixings, concealed materials, jointing and material compatibility, although much emphasis is put on creating the right architectural environment in terms of aesthetic and functional considerations.

As regards the quality of information, this is considered to be low – although there is a lot of it! Most of the information is based on standards, which is seen to be a sign of architectural abdication, with a passing of the specification back to the quantity surveyor. This results in a rationalised approach, with the corollary of a growth in the use of provisional sums. There is a tendency not to nominate unless it is unavoidable, giving the builder the final choice. Technical data and scientific evidence which would enhance the final specification is not in evidence. Moore concludes that critical facts for ensuring a sound basis upon which to measure the properties of similar products, or to understand the interaction between building components, fail to reach the specifiers. Since such facts are fundamental to any technology, as this volume has emphasised, this state of affairs is a major indictment of design professionals, and may have disastrous consequences for the built environment.

The conclusions of the CIOB paper centre on the finding that there appears to have been little change or improvement in the quality of objective construction information over the last ten years. The finger is pointed towards the education of those involved in specification, drawing and building processes. A look at course and syllabus components suggests a lack of input in these vital subjects. Much of the vital information produced and contained within a manufacturer's documentation fails to reach the true specifier. Manufacturers are advised to target their information to those people actually purchasing the products – who appear to be the builders. Contract documentation is seen to be woefully inadequate and it is stressed that it is necessary to improve this in conventional letting procedures. Builders should involve themselves in showing the direction in which change must take place. The use of standard references can limit innovation and severely hamper design initiatives. In order to avoid the use of standard references a more positive approach is required. It could mean that designers should take an active part in the creation of standards. The alternative, however, is a far greater use of performance specifications. This has the advantages of being based on scientific data and research evidence (therefore taking note of current innovations and developments) and, perhaps more significantly, of firmly placing the responsibility for the final decision with the builder – something which he often does now without formal recognition. Finally, the use of performance specifications draws on the knowledge and experience of specialists in all fields of construction.

One implication of the CIOB paper is that a greater use of named manufacturers could be included in specifications. In the traditional specification this could be harmful, in that it would completely bar the builder from decisions. A builder may encounter problems with a named manufacturer or supplier and this could materially affect the quality of the construction process, resulting in dissatisfaction with the technical considerations of construction details and performance. But if manufacturers opt for the award of Agrément Certificates they will be able to demonstrate that their product is meeting high standards of quality. Another implication of the CIOB paper is that standard references are to be avoided. Perhaps this is an extreme interpretation, but there *is* some concern over their levels of quality. They only meet minimum requirements and they can easily become out-dated, especially in this period of rapid technological change. Contrary to this viewpoint, the authors of the Building Regulations 1985 make particular reference to British Standards and Codes of Practice, while stating that there is an opportunity for alternatives to be presented for approval. Looking to past experience in the introduction of new ideas in construction it will be extremely difficult for innovation to gain acceptance.

In the light of the previous discussion the traditional role of specifications is under threat. If little use is being made of the specification owing to its inability to provide good information, why should it be prepared? Additionally, there are technological changes occurring in the standardisation of components. Complementary to this is the development of different forms of procurement for building work. There is an interplay between these three factors which will now be analysed with respect to its effect on specifications.

SPECIFICATION AND STANDARDISATION

There is an inexorable trend towards the increasing standardisation of construction materials, components and building structures. Softwood window frames are obtainable in common sizes from a range of manufacturers. In order to capture a large slice of a market a manufacturer will produce goods which can easily be made and can compete with others. If all these goods are in the same size range then production costs can be minimised. If all the window makers, for example, agree on standard sizes interchange can take place and customers requesting replacements can be sure of finding them at the right size. Therefore, one aspect of specification, determining size, is controlled by manufacturers. Manufacturers can also control quality by selling their products under generic headings, such as 'softwood', 'hardwood', 'UPVC' or 'aluminium'. It will be hard for the specifier to distinguish between each manufacturer under the headings unless a full scientific report is available on the particular material. The control over specification increases with developments in new materials, as manufacturers attempt to keep details of improvements to themselves in order to gain advantage over their competitors. Specifiers are more than likely to abrogate their responsibility when faced with a multitude of choices and a reluctance on the part of suppliers to give full information. This aspect is discussed further in the chapter on components in *Building Technology 3*. Many buildings are built using prefabricated parts, sections, elements, structural members and components. In effect, the designer selects from a catalogue of a whole range of products which, put together, will form an integral whole. There is little need for designer-initiated specifications as the majority of components will be from a manufacturer off a standard line. All that will be necessary from the designer are assembly drawings; any further information can be obtained from the manufacturer. The specification required can also be supplied by the manufacturer. Design/build companies can provide a complete building based on their own system of construction. Again, the specification is primarily in the control of the company, although there is generally scope for amendments.

With the advent of a wide variety of procurement procedures the traditional specification has not been seen as a useful document. In management fee and trade packages the onus is upon the competing specialist package contractors to meet the requirements of the designer and managing agent. These requirements may not necessarily be described in traditional specification clauses but by performance criteria. The contractor will have to demonstrate that he meets these requirements: one way in which this can be done is for him to produce his own specification. This then becomes a description to complement the drawings (details again produced by the contractor) and forms the basis of the levels of quality. The designer and/or managing agent assesses this specification against the set criteria. A reversal has taken place; the responsibility for specification and quality is firmly placed upon the contractor. One aspect of this is that the designer or managing agent has a choice of specifications, methods of attainment and price. Each will have satisfied the basic performance criteria, but can offer a range of real alternatives – something which a designer may not be able to provide. This should allow for development and innovations to be taken up. The quality of the specifications themselves should be high as they have been produced by a specialist in the field.

The interplay between systems of procurement, new technologies and manufacturers' standardisation could result in the demise of the traditional specification. This will not be universal, as many contracts will still be given on the basis of traditional specifications and drawings, with or without quantities, especially in the case of smaller alterations, refurbishments or conservation work. There is a trend towards specifications based on performance criteria, giving the responsibility for detailed compliance to the manufacturer of the product, the supplier or the organisation carrying out the work on site. In demonstrating their compliance, any of these three bodies might well prepare technical specifications. A technical specification details the properties of the product in scientific or measurable data. For example, a precast concrete beam's technical specification could include strength of concrete; type of aggregate and size; coefficient of expansion; deflection under specified loads; method of fixing; required bearing for support; and so on. Managing agents can use these specifications to assess the product or work package and check quality during manufacture, in the case of a product, and work on site in the case of trade activities.

COORDINATED PROJECT INFORMATION

We have considered how some specifications, bills of quantities, and other forms of project information have not been clear in the quality of information presented. This has led to problems in achieving quality on site. BRE Current Paper 7/81, *Quality control on building sites*, shows that there is a direct relationship between quality of information and quality of work. Good project information is highly likely to produce good quality, and the converse is true. The implication is that to improve quality levels on site an improvement in the project documentation would be of great benefit. In order to tackle this problem a committee was set up in 1979 by the Royal Institute of British Architects, Royal Institution of Chartered Surveyors, Building Employers Confederation and Association of Consulting Engineers. The aim was to improve the technical content and the effectiveness of documents. The committee has produced a set of conventions which give a comprehensive guide to the preparation of coordinated project documents. The conventions are set out in eight separate documents:

1. *Common arrangement of work sections for building works*, Building Project Information Committee (BPIC), 1987.
2. *Production drawings, a code of procedure for building works*, BPIC, 1987.
3. *Project Specification, a code of procedure for building works*, BPIC, 1987.

4. *National Building Specification*, NBS Ltd, reissued in new format 1988.
5. *National Engineering Specification*, NES Ltd, 1987.
6. *Standard Method of Measurement of Building Works*, Seventh Edition, RICS and BEC, 1987.
7. *Bills of Quantities, a code of procedure for building works*, RICS and BEC, 1987.
8. *SMM7 Standard Descriptions*, PSA, RICS and BEC, 1987.

The essence of this coordinated action is that a conventionalised reference system is given to items in specifications and bills of quantities. When determining the exact technical description of an item under the SMM7 method it is identified by a number which corresponds to the *NBS* specification. This reference is placed on the working drawings and arrowed to the construction detail. There is little or no written description on the drawing. In order to ascertain the description of the detail you are forced to refer directly to the specification clause. A guide book has been prepared which gives a worked example and should be referred to to obtain the full explanation of the conventions. (*Guide to Coordinated Project Information*, The Committee for Coordinated Project Information.) Here we shall comment on the purpose of the system and its purported improvements over existing practice. The guide lists a number of deficiencies in project information which can significantly contribute to major problems in the construction industry:

(a) the incidence of technical defects in finished buildings
(b) the frequency of poor quality of finished work, related to high maintenance costs
(c) the frequency of variations and consequential uncertainty as to the final cost
(d) the high level of claims being made by contractors
(e) the late completion of many contracts.

Research has demonstrated that much of this is due to poor project documentation, but what are the implications for the builder if this system is implemented? Three recommendations are given:

1. *Procedures for producing documents*, e.g. planning the set of drawings to minimise duplication and maximise use of copy negatives, techniques for coordinating services drawings, use of libraries of clauses as a systematic way of recording specification decisions.
2. *Technical content of documents*, e.g. annotation of drawings, detailed checklists for the content of project specifications, revised rules for measurement.
3. *Arrangement of documents*, e.g. structuring of drawn informa-

tion by type, use of the common arrangement for both specifications and quantities.

The implications for contractors fall under four main heads: 'general', 'tendering', 'programming' and 'quality control'. The latter is the major concern of this book.

Generally, the use of CPI should lead to a greater degree of certainty in pricing and building by ensuring that drawings are thoroughly prepared and complete. But it is recognised that the degree of preparedness will vary and the builder is advised to visit designers' offices to ascertain the reliability of the specification prior to tendering.

Tendering

This system is introduced concurrently with SMM7, which is in a simpler format than previous editions. Greater care needs to be taken in the preparation of documents for pricing, which should be reflected in higher standards for sub-contract documentation. Both contractors and sub-contractors should be provided with:

(a) measured quantities (with quantities contracts only)
(b) full specification information
(c) adequate drawings
(d) relevant preliminaries requirements.

Programming

On the programme the relevant specification references can be made next to the work activity. This will enable the information to be extended to aid management.

Quality Control

The claim is made that if the project information is well coordinated, comprehensive and provided in good time, the contractors' managers (and clients' clerks of works) need spend only minimal time on 'filling in the gaps'. The specification should set out clear requirements for samples, testing, inspections and approvals at defined stages in the work.

These sentiments have been clearly presented in this book, and many people within the industry concur with them. The best possible standards of performance have not yet been achieved. Whether or not a paper-based system will change attitudes and practice only time will tell, but at least coordinated project information is a step in the right direction. In order to obtain appreciable advances in quality this documentation needs a strong element of purpose and obligation. Whether or not the SMM7 is the right vehicle to carry this obligation and enforce a closer inspection of technical specification is debatable. In order to effectively specify there needs to be a full understanding of the behaviour of materials and construction detailing. A set of viable clauses still needs to be applied to the particular circumstances of a building's environment. This can only be carried out by competent technologists, who it is hoped will make optimum use of coordinated project information.

SUMMARY

This volume's introductory chapter discussed Pirsig's notion of quality. We have since examined the difference between substance and method. Specifications usually try to present both substantive and methodological aspects of construction in general descriptive terms. This has been found to be unsatisfactory, leading to incorrect interpretations, inappropriate standards and a confusion of responsibilities in the final decision on material or product. In this volume the value of performance as a means by which the quality of a building product can be assessed has been expounded. This is based on a classical, objective, analytical and scientific approach, aiming to create, first, an acceptable range of measures, and, second, a use of these measures as a basis for comparison and evaluation. A scientific approach is necessary in order to make sense of data and information so that a full understanding can be obtained. The methodology is the means by which the understanding can be fully exploited, and it is in this area that much improvement needs to be achieved. The linking factor between substance and method is performance. By addressing our attention to the assessment and measure of performance a clearer knowledge of materials, components and processes can be obtained. This does mean that a change in attitude is necessary. The paramount aim in building would be to ensure that the fitness for purpose of the structure and of construction procedures are first clearly defined, and, second, effectively achieved. Concern for quality in product, material, decision and workmanship should be at the forefront of aims and objectives. In providing this quality the construction team can work in harmony and efficiency, thereby increasing productivity – and consequently earnings. Society will have buildings which perform to agreed criteria and which are fit for their purposes. They will perform safely and well.

The expectations of industrialised societies are constantly rising with respect to standards and quality. As standards of living increase so too does the demand for higher quality levels. Quality in comfort levels, quality in providing a climatic barrier, quality in ensuring the fire safety of buildings, all these are of increasing concern to the owners and occupiers of buildings. Society is more critical and can voice its concern over the internal and external environment of buildings. There is a greater awareness of the way that buildings, their components and services, should perform. Builders and designers should be far more knowledgeable about the wealth of information now easily obtainable on the performance of materials, components and structures. There is no excuse for technologists to plead ignorance with respect to failures, in a great many instances. Many defects and failures are avoidable if competent research is carried out to ascertain the integrity of a material or component at the design stage, and if standards of workmanship are upheld in the course of the installation process. Information is not lacking – unlike its application. The construction industry needs to improve performance in all its facets. The quest for quality must be an underlying and paramount objective.

QUESTIONS

1. Discuss how it might be possible to assess all building technology decisions from the viewpoint of performance.
2. Assess the role of specifications in the desire for quality.
3. What advantages are there in making extensive reference to published standards in specifications?
4. Discuss the possibility of the majority of building materials and products being governed by standards and prescribed technical specifications.

Part Five
CASE STUDIES

20. Five Construction Case Studies

INTRODUCTION

The following construction case studies are intended to focus attention on some of the issues raised and discussed in this volume. All are based on actual buildings or incidents, mainly in the UK but also in other countries. In considering these cases two aspects should be borne in mind. First, their connection to principles discussed in theory in the preceding chapters, which should now be thought of as they would in practice, and, second, their function as illustrations providing a basis for further analysis, development and evaluation. They should be read critically in order to discover their limitations, but should also be seen as a basis for developing further understanding and knowledge. We can learn from good and bad practice alike.

CONSTRUCTION STUDY ONE – DETERIORATION TO A BLOCK OF FLATS

The following study of deterioration in the façade of a block of flats demonstrates the destructive effect of climate upon a building.

Site and Structure

The building is a six-storey, steel-framed structure with concrete ring beams at each floor level. The cladding is in brick, but at some time after its construction in the late 1930s a rendering has been applied. The flats are situated on the south coast of England, facing the sea, and some residents claim that during heavy storms and seas the building vibrates.

Problems

On examination the rendering was found to be up to 50mm thick in places, with no movement joints, either vertical or horizontal. This rigid external coat applied to an already rigid building inevitably caused cracks to appear when the structure flexed. These cracks allowed rain and other forms of moisture to penetrate the structure, causing spalling of the concrete, which was subject to extensive carbonation and chloride attack, and corrosion of the reinforcement and the steel frame. Additionally, evidence was found of wall tie failure in the brick cladding. Balcony parapets were ready to fall; the metal windows of the building were severely corroded and warped; wet rot had taken hold inside. At some point, repairs to the rendering had been carried out, in the form of minimal patching using a system of tar-coated hessian laid as a sub-strata upon which a sand/cement render was applied. When the rendering was stripped away from the brickwork water literally oozed out.

Three general points can be made here. First, the building is in a very exposed position. Second, the construction and materials used were not suitable to the task. Third, the previous remedial work carried out on the building was totally inadequate.

Solutions

New expansion joints were cut into the rendering, and cracks were cut out and replaced. The hessian-based patches were also cut out and replaced with stainless steel lathing and again rendered. It was not possible to remove completely the render coat to expose the bricks, as the bricks were found to be heavily hacked and indented to give a mechanical lay. New joints were cut around the window frames to mitigate the effects of movement around the openings. The concrete ring beam was cut back to sound concrete, and new reinforcement bars were added. The concrete cover was then recast. The heavily corroded downstands around the exposed balconies were hacked away and replaced with downstands of a much shallower design. New resin anchor-wall ties were fitted, placed to restore stability following the corrosion of the old wall ties.

The deterioration of the building fabric, with the subsequent vulnerability of the structural frame to attack, was accelerated by inadequate cover to the reinforcement, causing the concrete to spall. Also, during the construction of the building, calcium chloride was added to the concrete which then began to eat away at the reinforcement. Salt-laden moisture from the sea water could therefore pass through the cracks in the render to attack the covered structure below. The repair work remedied this problem.

Legislation

An added problem illustrated by this case study is the effect of legislation on the construction process. The twelve flats were tenanted – and therefore occupied under lease. The Landlord and Tenant Act 1985, Section 20, requires that where any expenditure payable by a maintenance fund exceeds £500, or is greater than 25 times the rent of flats in a building, then a notice should be served on all long-term leaseholders. Twenty-eight days notice of the proposed expenditure by the landlord allows time for the leaseholders to comment on or object to the proposed works. The leaseholders' views should be taken into account by the landlord. The work to be done should be clearly stated by the landlord, and at least two competitive tenders obtained. The successful contractor should be named. The leaseholders have to put up the money in advance, and in the case of non-payment the penalty is forfeiture of a lease. This money is paid into a separate bank deposit account and can only be drawn on the production of three signatures – those of the freeholding company, the managing agent and the representative of the residents. In the case of the block of flats the leaseholders were required to pay £6000 each, with additional costs of up to a further £3000 if their flats faced the sea, where the windows had to be replaced. The total costs in terms of 1987 prices can be estimated at £450,000. After the work the flats may be expected to have appreciated in value by about one-third of their former value, becoming worth an average £10,000 each. Thus an outlay of up to £9000 per flat may result in a gain in value. This, of course, can only be realised on sale of the lease.

The Landlord and Tenant Act has wide implications, and may encourage landlords to undertake maintenance and remedial work with increasing vigour, as they can legally apportion the costs to the leaseholders. This is good news for those concerned with the state of the built environment, but perhaps not for the tenants who have to find the money.

Supplementary questions

1. Describe a suitable cladding to the steel framed structure which could be used as a preferred solution if the building was to remain weather-tight for a further 50 years with negligible maintenance, giving reasons for the choice.
2. Should the concept of apportioning repair cost to owners or

occupiers be applied legislatively to ensure repairs are carried out to buildings exhibiting major defects? In this case inspectors may be appointed to check buildings and, if necessary, issue notices to their owners demanding they carry out remedial work in order to preserve them. This would be additional to the present legislation covering dangerous structures, and would refer to the *general* condition of the building. Are there benefits in this for the building technologist? Or is it simply an infringement of people's rights?

3. In the granting of mortgages, most contracts state that the mortgagee must maintain the property adequately. Should this stipulation be vigorously enforced? What might the implications be for new house construction if builders knew that the commitment to adhere to maintenance clauses regarding deterioration of the fabric were a major factor in the granting of a mortgage?

CONSTRUCTION STUDY TWO – EARTH-SHELTERED BUILDINGS

Earth-sheltered buildings offer a solution to some of the problems of climatically induced material deterioration. This type of construction is set either completely or partially into the ground, ideally on a slope so as to reduce the amount of excavation necessary; this also allows some vertical walls to stand free of the surrounding earth, enabling easy access and natural lighting in the conventional plane. The main source of lighting to covered areas of the building is by roof lights. Earth often covers the roof and surrounds the majority of the external wall surfaces. Usually the walls are constructed from concrete produced *in situ* or from concrete blocks, with added insulation and waterproofing. The roof structure is concrete, except for the roof lights, and is again insulated. One such house will be described here.

Site and Structure

The entrance is onto an open area containing a swimming pool and indoor landscaping with flagged floors and vegetation. Opening off this area are the bedrooms, kitchens, bathrooms and recreation rooms. The living area has a vertical external wall with a wide sliding window facing south. The walls are constructed of 200mm thermalite blocks, with precast concrete blocks used as structural units retaining the earth. The roof insulation is below the roof structure, creating a 'cold' roof. A drainage system channels rain-water and ground-water away from the building. The levels of insulation are not high, and when built in the early 1970s the present concern for energy conservation was not foreseen.

The owner thought that the swimming pool would create high humidity problems, and so incorporated fans and a boiler with excess capacity for additional warm air. In practice the humidity had been found to vary only between 51% and 56%, which is quite acceptable. The internal temperature has also proved relatively constant, varying between 17°C in winter and 22°C in summer. A wider variation in temperatures might have produced a greater humidity variation, with the possibility of excess condensation – which is not a problem in this house.

Advantages

Although the house was not conceived in terms of energy saving, and does not contain what are now considered to be good levels of insulation, it nevertheless produces savings. Bearing in mind that this earth-sheltered house has relatively high floor to ceiling heights, especially in the pool areas, the volume to be heated is high. The energy costs, however, have proved to be roughly half of those in traditional detached houses of equivalent areas and volumes. This finding has been borne out by research into earth-sheltered buildings in Australia and the United States of America.

The problems arising where a building functions as a climatic barrier have been circumnavigated to a great extent. The building is not extensively exposed to wind, rain, frost or snow. It snuggles below ground level with only a few exposed elements, namely the roof lights and the south-facing windows. These south-facing windows are an advantage, moreover, as their solar gain is greater than the internal thermal loss, when taken over a full year. The earth surround cushions the building from all but the most extreme effects of the climate, and this enables almost complete planning and control of the internal environment. Heating systems, in such a case, can be designed and installed on the basis of almost complete control over temperature. The use of insulation in the walls and the roof can prevent virtually any heat loss (there is definitely no need to consider exposure factors in the calculations of heat loss to the buried walls). The use of well-planned drainage systems coupled with adequate waterproofing will prevent any ingress of moisture due to rainfall penetrating the earth, therefore the effects of water on the structure are minimised.

Deterioration due to climatic effects should be greatly reduced in earth-sheltered buildings. Careful choice of exposed elements such as roof lights and window frames should eliminate undue deterioration. Frost can penetrate the surrounding earth but its effect on the structure is minimal. There is a possibility of deterioration to the buried structure caused by chemicals leaking through the soil with the drainage of rain. The soil should therefore be tested for the presence of any damaging chemicals. If these are found, two courses of action are possible: first, the removal of the soil and its replacement with uncontaminated material, and, second, the use of materials and/or protective layers which resist the chemicals' effects. The latter solution is probably cheapest. If precautions are taken then deterioration should be non-existent.

Supplementary questions

1. For what reasons is it not always possible to construct this type of house? As far as performance criteria go there are many advantages, but these can be completely offset by planning decisions, land availability and social constraints.
2. A useful exercise to complete in relation to the study of earth-sheltered houses is the preparation of a report directed to a client putting forward the performance advantages of this type of construction. If there are any disadvantages, then the report should mention these but counter them with potential benefits.

CONSTRUCTION STUDY THREE – A FIRE IN A SINGLE-STOREY RESIDENTIAL BUILDING

Structure

The building was constructed using the CLASP (Consortium of Local Authorities Special Project) system: a light steel framework with a plasterboard lining and mineral fibre insulation. A suspended ceiling of plasterboard panels provided a continuous open space over most of the building's area, to a depth of 500mm. This space was used to house the services. The complete residential building was divided into five separate accommodation units, and was used as an old people's home.

Spread of the fire

The fire was probably caused by a lighted cigarette left in one of the bedrooms. The fire grew to a flashover state before it was noticed. It entered the roof void and consequently spread to the other units in the building along the linking corridors driven by a prevailing wind. Most of the damage and loss of life (18 people in total) occurred in units remote from the source of fire. The fire spread particularly quickly because of the lack of barriers in the roof void. Additionally, there was no compartmentation between the units, and the ceiling panels themselves quickly succumbed to the fire.

The need for cavity/void barriers in horizontal spaces is evident from this example, and regulations now insist upon them in the UK. Even though separate units were built in this case, there ought to have been some form of compartmentation when these were linked together. As this was a special-risk building housing old people, there should have been better fire detection measures, to alert people more quickly. A similar problem was a contributory reason for loss of life in a fire in a French old people's home, when the slow rate of evacuation led to undue loss of life, with a total of 24 fatalities.

The use of a sprinkler system in CLASP-built buildings may not help prevent the spread of fire, as this may occur above the sprinklers themselves. This illustrates a general problem with roof fires: they cannot be controlled by sprinklers. A further example is that of a very large single-storey building used for jet engine repairs, which caught fire at roof-level. The building area was 14 hectares, and its length was 1.4km, with floor to ceiling heights of 11–18m. There were 65 sprinkler systems, manual alarms and stand-pipes for hoses. The sprinklers were operated manually but they had no effect as they were 300mm below the underside of the roof. They were turned off, leaving fire raging for three days until a trench was dug and the fire controlled. This resulted in the loss of one-third of the building's workshops. Two points are self-evident from this fire: first, that sprinklers cannot help control fires in roof spaces, and, second, that a lack of compartmentation in a building can make it exceedingly difficult to control a fire. In this case there was no loss of life, but damage costs were estimated to be $138 million US. People may be evacuated quickly from a building, but in any fire there is the possibility of loss of life, or injury, to the fire fighters. This factor is often not given due consideration in the incorporation of safety measures. The risk to fighters is highest in older buildings with masonry and timber floors and roofs. These may prevent fire spread and give some fire protection, but in the case of a major conflagration the building can become structurally unstable. A department store fire in summer 1987 in Madrid, Spain, for example, caused the death of three firemen when a floor collapsed.

A number of issues have developed from a study of the initial incident in a single-storey system-built old people's home. Two important points have been noted, and are worth repeating: first, buildings need compartmentation, even when conceived as separate but linked units, and, second, fire can spread through roof spaces quickly and unseen unless fire protection barriers are installed.

Supplementary questions

1. Consider the value of placing sprinklers at a level just below a roof space, especially if the roof space itself could have a high fire load owing to its materials of construction or the services that run through it.
2. Consider the use of appropriate detection and alarm systems. The capacity of people to react in the case of fire should directly determine the fire safety system. For example, it can be argued that a workshop utilised by physically or mentally handicapped people should have extensive fire safety measures, over and above those deemed suitable for able-bodied and competent occupants.

CONSTRUCTION STUDY FOUR – THE INTERNAL/ EXTERNAL ENVIRONMENT INTERFACE

The case study here is a block of 20 flats constructed in London of traditional load-bearing cavity brick and block, with intermediate cross walls supporting *in situ* reinforced concrete floors. The walls are built from 100mm Leca blocks, with 100mm polystyrene-bonded bead insulation and an outer leaf of 105mm facing brick. The ground floor is 75mm sand/cement screed laid over 50mm polystyrene insulation on a 150mm *in situ* concrete slab. The concrete upper floors are overlaid with 22mm chipboard on 50mm × 50mm battens on resilient quilt. The windows and doors are of high-performance softwood, all with sealed, double-glazed units. Ventilation is provided by a trickle ventilator positioned in the head of the window/door frame, and within internal halls by a louvre vent with a duct leading to an air brick in the outside wall. Kitchens and bathrooms have mechanical extractor fans. The roof is slated, using standard battens and sarking felt sitting on standard softwood trussed rafters. A 12.7mm Gyproc wall-board and plaster skin supports 140mm glass-fibre quilt insulation.

These flats were built on an energy saving concept, the idea being to bring about a reduction in heating load by using high levels of insulation. This insulation would lessen the energy requirements, enabling a lower output, allowing a cheaper heating system to be installed. The main living room and bedrooms are at the back, facing south, with only kitchens and bathrooms facing north. By using large windows and balconies on the south-facing sides advantage is taken of maximum solar gain. Because of the building's large surface area with stepped façades, the heat losses might be greater than normal in a square building of the same capacity.

A heating system was chosen which can efficiently cater for small loads, and this was used in conjunction with a thermal store which can even out fluctuating demands. The system's advantages are said to be that a smaller boiler can then be used, which reduces installation costs and is more efficient at low output levels, thus reducing running costs and taking up less space; its compactness reduces heat loss and therefore running costs; it has a fast response; the unit can be fed directly from a mains water supply; in small dwellings it is also more flexible, without the constraints of a conventional flued gas convector.

The extra cost (at 1988 prices) of achieving this lower energy solution is £3 per flat – a negligible amount. The savings are purported to be 45% for a two bedroom flat and 52% for a one bedroom flat – cheaper than conventional full-house heating with minimum insulation, that is insulation which meets the present (1987) Building Regulation requirements for walls and roofs.

Supplementary questions

1. What are the implications of constructing external walls of a greater thickness than normal cavity walls? (normal cavity walls range from 260mm to over 300mm in thickness.) Does the installation of insulation require special care and attention? Is there a likelihood of accelerated deterioration using the construction described? If the benefits are so obvious why are not all new houses and flats built in this way?

CONSTRUCTION STUDY FIVE – FIRE IN A SHOPPING MALL

Site and structure

The shops complex covers approximately 2.2 hectares, with shops on several floors, a market, a hotel, restaurants, a multi-storey car park, basement · storage and service area and a restaurant incorporated into a 140 metres high beacon. Mostly constructed in reinforced concrete beams, columns and floors, the walls separating the shops are of lightweight block faced with plaster.

The fire

A fire originated in a shop with a suspended ceiling over its retail area, reportedly constructed of Class 1 tiles on a timber frame. The soffits of the service void of the covered market projected partly into the ceiling void, and were structurally rolled steel joists covered with sprayed asbestos supporting lightweight concrete blocks. A barrier of asbestos boards and glass fibre insulation was placed in the ceiling void to separate mall from shop. An unknown type of wall board lined the shop walls and the front had a plate glass window. In the room at the back of the shop used as staff room and stock area a timber mezzanine floor was used for additional storage.

There were no smoke reservoirs with means of extraction included in the original design, but two moveable, glass-reinforced plastics/GRP roof-lights were installed above a stairwell in a covered square, with electric motors to retract them. At the time of construction this was thought sufficient to cope with smoke-logging. Only the basement had sprinklers, although the fire brigade did recommend that the whole complex should be thus equipped. There were smoke detectors in the market hall, plant rooms, lift motor rooms, sub-stations and at the top of the beacon.

The cause of the fire was recorded as follows: 'defective fluorescent light caused overheating and ignition of choke which in turn ignited combustible material adjacent to mounting'.

The damage was extensive. In the shop where the fire originated most of the flammable contents, wall and ceiling linings had been destroyed. The plaster had come off most of the walls and there was damage to the concrete of the reinforced beams and to the steel joists supporting the service void to the market. On the other side of the mall a shop had severe heat and smoke damage throughout, but there were signs of burning on a mezzanine floor and fire damage to the timber ceiling linings. Some plaster was missing from a partition. In the mall there were severe fire damage to the suspended ceiling with a lot of the steel grid and some of the ventilation trunking hanging down near to the shop of fire origin. The shops on either side had some fire damage but were mainly affected by heat and smoke. Damage diminished towards both ends of the mall although the plate glass windows of many shops were broken, causing severe smoke damage. Heavy smoke deposits occurred on most surfaces with lighter stains some distance away from the fire, but still within the complex. Some shops on the floors directly above the fire suffered cracks to the floors and walls due to the expansion of the structural frame, with smoke spreading through this route affecting their contents. The upper floor malls suffered smoke damage to some extent.

The fire brigade had considerable difficulty in fighting the fire owing to the presence of smoke in the malls. In the mall outside the shop the smoke was quickly down to floor level. People had to be evacuated from a nearby hotel due to smoke penetration. All upper floors were smoke logged. About an hour after the initial alarm, and attendance by the fire brigade, one of the roof lights was manually opened. This improved conditions. When the second roof light was opened conditions again improved. The smoke hampered fire fighting and the officers had to use breathing apparatus; a number suffered heat exhaustion and the effects of smoke.

Morgan, H.P. and Savage, N.P., *A study of a large fire in a covered shopping complex: St John Centre 1977*, CP 10/80, details the investigation of this fire and puts forward these conclusions. The complex was built prior to the publication of the *Fire Prevention Guide on Town Centre Development*. There were no sprinklers or detectors in the affected shops or malls. The fire was first detected visually in the shop of origin. When this shop-front failed the complex filled with smoke within minutes. The fire's peak output of $27 \pm 6\text{MW}$ far exceeded the 5MW currently assumed from sprinkler-controlled fires. The spread of hot gases carried the fire across the mall to a shop opposite the origin. There was evidence that a flowing smoke layer meeting a transverse barrier, for example a wall, had deepened locally. The pronounced deepening apparent opposite the shop of fire origin suggests that this effect could endanger shops fronting on to a mall opposite the shop originally on fire. Experimental work is needed to establish the magnitude of this effect. The provisions for the natural venting of smoke had not operated until after the fire had become smaller. Approximate calculations indicate that the upper malls became smoke-logged less than one minute after the smoke passed from a mall into an enclosed square. The middle-storey malls probably became smoke-logged in 3–5 minutes. Further calculations indicate that even if the roof vents had operated, the upper malls would still have become seriously affected by smoke.

The fire occurred outside normal shop opening hours in the early evening and there were no casualties. The biggest problem was smoke-logging. This would have considerably hindered means of escape. The absence of sprinklers in the shop allowed the fire to develop, and allowed further development in the malls. Since this fire the need for smoke detectors, sprinklers and smoke vents has been recognised and they should now be incorporated in any similar schemes.

SUPPLEMENTARY QUESTIONS

1. Who should be responsible for the evacuation of people from

the complex in the event of fire – the complex management or individual shop managers? Should smoke detectors and alarms be directly connected to the fire brigade station?

2. A complex such as this could be simulated/modelled to assess the flow and possible damage caused by smoke and fire. Should this be a mandatory condition for statutory approvals?

3. There was evidence of structural damage to the building, for example cracks in the concrete floors; what investigation procedures need to be carried out to assess the overall extent of the damage, and what type of remedial work should be done?

4. In general terms, what might be the overall effect on the rate of deterioration to the building after a fire such as this?

5. Considering this case, should emphasis be placed on passive fire resistance or on active fire prevention measures?

References and Further Reading

ABBA CONSULTANTS, *Computer-based energy management in buildings*, Pitman, 1982.

ADAMS, E.C., *Science in building*, Vols. 1, 2 and 3, Hutchinson, 1985.

ADDLESON, L., *Materials for Building*, Vols. 1, 2 and 3, Iliffe Books, 1972.

ADDLESON, L., *Materials for Building*, Vol. 4, *Heat and fire and their effects*, Newnes-Butterworths, 1976.

ADDLESON, L., *Building failures: A guide to diagnosis, remedy and prevention*, The Architectural Press, 1982.

THE AQUA GROUP, *Fire and building: A guide for the design team*, Collins, 1984.

ANGUS, T.C., *The control of indoor climate*, Pergamon, 1968.

AYNSLEY, R.M., MELBOURNE, W. and VICKERY, B.J., *Architectural Aerodynamics*, Applied Science Publishers, 1977. *Workmanship factors associated with CP 110 – the structural use of concrete*. CIOB Site Management Information Service Paper No. 88, 1981.

BAND, G., DOWN, M.R., BRANDON, W.D.S. and AUN, C.S., *Energy performance of buildings*, CRC Press, 1984.

BEECH, J.C. and SAUNDERS, C.K., *The performance of building gaskets*, BRE CP 3183.

BENTLEY, M.J.C., *Quality control on building sites*. BRE CP 7/81.

BRACKLEY, G., *The variability of the measurement of water tightness in joints*, CP 6/83.

BROWNE, R., 'The science of decay', *Building* 19, September 1986, pp. 82–3.

BUILDING TECHNOLOGY SPECIAL, 'Fire and security', *Building* 16, January 1987.

BURGESS, K.S., *Computer programs for energy in buildings*, Design Office Consortium, 1979.

BURBERRY, P., *Building for energy conservation*, Architectural Press/Halsted Press, 1978.

BURBERRY, P., *Environment and services*, Mitchell, 1975.

BURBERRY, P., *Practical thermal design in buildings*, Mitchell, 1983.

BRE, *Wall cladding: designing to minimise defects due to inaccuracies and movements*, Digest 225, Building Research Establishment, 1970.

BRE, *Repairing brickwork*, Digest 200, Building Research Establishment, 1977.

BRE, *Building Materials*, Medical and Technical Publishing Co., 1973.

BRE, *Building Performance*, Building Research Establishment Digests Vol. 3, HMSO, 1983.

BRE, *Building Components and Materials*, Building Research Establishment Digests Vol. 2, HMSO, 1983.

BRE, *Wall cladding defects and their diagnosis*, Digest 217, Building Research Establishment, 1978.

BRE, *Assessment of damage in low-rise buildings – with particular reference to progressive foundation movement*, Digest 251, Building Research Establishment, 1981.

BRE, *Installation of wall ties in existing constructions*, Digest 257, Building Research Establishment 1982.

BRE, *Common defects in low-rise traditional housing*, Digest 268, Building Research Establishment, 1982.

BRE, *Reducing the risk of pest infestation: design recommendations and literature review*, Digest 238, Building Research Establishment, 1980.

BRE, *Concrete in sulphate-bearing soils and ground waters*, Digest 250, Building Research Establishment, 1981.

BRE DIGESTS, *Building materials*, The Construction Press, 1977.

BRE DIGESTS, *Building defects and maintenance*, MTP Construction, 1974.

BRE BUILDING RESEARCH SERIES, *Building failure*, The Construction Press, 1978.

CHANDLER, I.E., *Materials management on construction sites*, The Construction Press, 1978.

CHUDLEY, R., *The maintenance and adaptation of buildings*, Longman, 1981.

COAD, W.J., *Energy engineering and management for building systems*, Van Nostrand Reinhold, 1982.

CONKLIN, G., *The weather conditioned house*, Van Nostrand Reinhold, 1982.

COWELL, A.S.T., *agency – an aspect of long-term maintenance*, CIOB Maintenance Information Service Paper No. 5, 1978.

DAVISON, L.R. and C.J., *Building defects associated with ground conditions: a review*, CIOB Technical Information Service, 1986.

DERRICOTT, R. and CLUSSIKE, S.S., *Energy conservation and thermal insulation*, John Wiley and Sons, 1981.

DOE and FIRE OFFICERS' COMMITTEE, *Fire resistance requirements for buildings – a new approach*, Proceedings of the Symposium held in London, 28 September 1971, HMSO, 1973.

EVERETT, A., *Materials*, Mitchell, 1984.

FLETCHER, K.E., *The conformance of some common building*

products with British Standards, CP 4/83.

GARDNER, P., *Energy management systems in buildings*, Energy Publications/Cambridge Information and Research Services, 1984.

GATWICK, R.J., *Dampness in buildings*, Crosby Lockwood Staples, 1974.

GROOME, D.J., *Noise, buildings and people*, Pergamon, 1977.

GROOME, D.J., *Noise and the design of buildings and services*, Construction Press, 1982.

HARPER, D., *Building: The Process and the Product*, The Construction Press, 1978.

HIGGINS, D.D., *Removal of stains and growth from concrete*, CIOB Technical Information Service Paper No. 26, 1983.

JOHNSON, R., *Foundations problems associated with low-rise housing*, Parts 1 and 2, CIOB Technical Information Service Papers Nos. 61 and 62, 1986.

KING, H. and OSBOURN, D., *Components*, Mitchell, 1985.

KNUDSEN, V.O. and HARRIS, C.M., *Acoustical designing in architecture*, American Institute of Physics/Acoustical Society of America, 1978.

KYTE, C.T., *Laboratory analysis as an aid to the diagnosis of rising damp*, CIOB Technical Information Service Paper No. 35, 1984.

LACY, R.E., *Climate and building in Britain*, for Department of the Environment/Building Research Establishment, HMSO, 1977.

LANGDON-THOMAS, C.J., *Fire safety in buildings: Principles and Practice*, Adam and Charles Black, 1972.

MALHOTRA, H.L., *Design of fire resisting structures*, Surrey University Press, 1982.

MALHOTRA, H.L., *Fire safety in buildings*, for Building Research Establishment/Department of the Environment, HMSO, 1987.

MARCHANT, E.W., *Fire and building*, Medical and Technical Publishing Co., 1972.

MARSH, P., *Thermal insulation and condensation*, The Construction Press, 1979.

MARTIN, B., *Joists in building*, George Godwin, 1977.

MAYO, A.P., REDWELL, D.F.G. and MORGAN, J.W.W., *Trussed rafter roofs*, BRE CP 5/893.

MCMILLAN, R., *Environmental science in building*, The Macmillan Press, 1983.

MILLS, E.D., *Building maintenance and preservation*, Butterworths, in association with The Building Centre Trust, 1980.

MONAGHAN, T.J., *Practical application of quality assurance to construction*, CIOB Technical Information Service Paper No. 80, 1987.

MOORE, J.F.A., *The performance of cavity wall ties*, CP 3/81.

MOORE, R.F., *Specification and purchasing within traditional contracting*, CIOB Technical Information Service Paper No. 82, 1987.

MORRIS, W.A. and READ, R.E.H., *Appraisal of passive fire precautions in large panel system flats and maisonettes*, Ip 18/86. BRE.

MORGAN, H.P. and SAVAGE, N.P., *A study of a large fire in a covered shopping complex: St Johns Centre*, 1977, CP 10/80. BRE.

NBA (NATIONAL BUILDING AGENCY), *Common building defects: Diagnosis and Remedy*, Construction Press, 1979.

PAGE, J.K., 'Weather as a factor in building design and construction', in *Progress in construction science and technology*, edited by Burgess, R.A., Harroban, P.J. and Simpson, J.W., Medical and Technical Publishing Co., 1971.

PAWLEY, M., *Garbage Housing*, Architectural Press, 1975.

OPPENHEIM, D., *Small solar buildings in cool northern climates*, The Architectural Press, 1981.

RANDALL, R.H., *Building defects and feedback on PSA*, CIOB Maintenance Information Service Paper, No. 4, 1978.

RAYSDALE, L.A. and RAYNHAM, E.A., *Building Materials Technology*, Edward Arnold, 1972.

RANKIN, I., *Quality control and tolerances for internal finishes in building*, CIOB Technical Information Service Paper No. 2, 1982.

READ, R.E.H., *Fire risks on high-rise buildings*, CP 1/79.

RIBA PUBLICATIONS, *Solar technology for building*, Vols. 1 and 2, Proceedings of the International Conference 25–29 July 1977 at Royal Institute of British Architects, RIBA Publications, 1978.

SCHOLES, W.E., *The propagation and screening of traffic noise*, BRE CP 26/74.

SCHWOLSKY, R. and WILLIAMS, J.I., *The builder's guide to solar construction*, McGraw-Hill, 1982.

SEELEY, I.H., *Building maintenance*, The Macmillan Press, 1982.

SHERRATT, A.F.C., *Integrated environment in building design*, Applied Science Publications, 1974.

SILCOCK, A., *Fires in dwellings – an investigation of actual fires*, Part IV: *Fires in BISF Houses*, CP 9/81.

SIMPSON, J.W. and HORROBIN, P.J., *The weathering and performance of building materials*, Medical and Technical Publishing Co., 1970.

SINNOTT, R., *Safety and security in building design*, Collins, 1985.

SMITH, R.N.B., *Condition appraisals and their use*, CIOB Technical Information Service Paper No. 5, 1985.

SMITH, E.E. and HARMATHY, T.Z., *Design of buildings for fire safety*, American Society for Testing and Materials, 1979.

SPENCE, R.J.S. and COOK, D.J., *Building materials in developing countries*, John Wiley and Sons, 1985.

STAVELY, H.S., *Structural Surveys*, CIOB Maintenance Information Service Paper No. 15, 1981.

STAVELEY, H.S., *Measured dimensional surveys*, CIOB Technical Information Service Paper No. 44, 1984.

STEADMAN, P., *Energy, environment and building*, Cambridge University Press, 1975.

SZOKOLAY, S.V., *Solar energy for building*, The Architectural Press, 1975.

SZOKOLAY, S.V., *Solar energy for building*, The Architectural Press/Halsted Press/John Wiley and Sons, 1976.

TAYLOR, G., *Maintenance and repair of structural concrete*, CIOB Maintenance Information Service Paper No. 87, 1981.

TRADA, *Wood Information*, Timber Research and Development Association, 1980.

TURNBULL, J., *A guide to commissioning maintenance manuals*, CIOB Technical Information Service Paper No. 83, 1987.

UNDERWOOD, G., *The Security of Buildings*, The Architectural Press, 1984.

UTLEY, W.A. and ALPHEY, R.S., *A survey of the sound insulation between dwellings in modern building constructions*, BLT CP 52/74.

VAN STRAATEN, J.F., *Thermal performance of buildings*, Elsevier Publishing Company, 1967.

VALE, B.R., *The autonomous house*, Thames and Hudson, 1975.

WATTS, J.W., *Supervision of installation*, Mitchell, 1982.

WATSON, D.A., *Construction Materials and Processes*, McGraw-Hill, 1972.

WATSON, D. and LABS, K., *Climatic design*, McGraw-Hill, 1983.

WELLER, J.W., and YOULE, A., *Thermal energy conservation: Building and services design*, Applied Science Publishers, 1981.

Index

Agrément Certificate 152, 191, 204
Allen, W. 123
Aqua Group 123
Automatic sprinklers 129, 150, 165, 172, 217, 220

Burberry, P. 51
Building Regulations 50, 95, 118, 128, 139, 145, 152, 160, 165, 179, 184, 192, 204
Building Research Establishment 30, 36, 46, 48, 60, 63, 88, 94, 107, 108, 118
British Standards 32, 36, 63, 123, 150, 153, 179, 189, 202
Bricks 87

Chartered Institute of Building Services Engineers 34, 67
CI/SfB 197
Climate, macro 18, 32
meso, 18, 26
micro 18, 29, 46
crypto 18, 34, 46
Comfort 57
Computers 24, 44, 55, 65, 72, 100, 143, 161
Concrete 89, 142, 186, 206, 212
Condensation 53f
Construction process 35
Cost 105, 124, 145, 155, 166, 172
Co-ordinated project information 100, 206ff

Daylight factor 64, 70f
Degree days 33, 52
Design 17, 42, 62, 69, 94, 100, 122, 136, 142, 152, 155
Deteriorology 113

Energy 19, 29, 40, 50, 54

Fire, compartmentation 144, 165
engineers 163, 170
flashover 135, 137
grading 135
hazard 139
insurance 123, 130, 145, 166, 172
safety 119ff, 125, 129, 160ff, 164, 166, 169
resistance 140, 156
function 43

Groome, D.J. 55

Harmony 13
Harper, D. 38
Humidity 21, 53

'Intelligent' buildings 784

Kyte, C.T. 112

Life cycle costing 69

Maintenance 14, 20, 81, 93, 96, 193
Malhotra, H.L. 140, 160, 173
Marchant, E.W. 161, 167
Moore, R.F. 203

National Building Specification 197
Noise 55ff
Nugarajan, R. 186

Performance, definition 9
  general 63, 70, 80, 114
  specification 183f, 203
  standards 58, 64, 85, 192, 205
Pirsig, R. 10, 180
Pollution 25, 75
Property Services Agency 106

Quality 10ff, 37, 97, 115, 178, 180, 186, 199, 203, 108
Quality Assurance 14, 97f, 115, 190

Radon 68
Rainfall 22, 30
Randall, R.H. 106

Rankin, I. 98
Research 43, 57, 117, 120, 170, 192

Scarman, Lord 81
'Sick' buildings 68
Solar radiation 33
Sound insulation 55
Smith, R.N.B. 103
Smoke control 145, 151, 157
Standard Methods of Measurement 196
Standardisation 186ff, 104
Stavely, H.S. 102

Temperature 21, 28
TERN Project 47
Technology, high 42, 47
Timber 84
'Tight' building shell 67
Thermal resistance 50, 53
Thomas, H.M. 179
Trade-offs 69f, 120, 165, 172

Vandalism 80
Value 13
Ventilation 66

Wind 23, 28, 31f
Workmanship 37, 47, 59f, 146, 158, 195, 200